Physical activity in our lives

Qualitative research among disabled people

Sue Arthur

Helen Finch

Social & Community Planning Research

Acknowledgements

We would like to thank all the men and women who agreed to give up their time to take part in this study and to acknowledge the role of Jill Keegan who undertook many of the interviews, Marion Clayden and Virginia Swain who helped with the analysis, and Alana Diamond of the Health Education Authority who oversaw the study.

Health Education Authority
Trevelyan House
30 Great Peter Street
London SW1P 2HW

Printed in Great Britain

ISBN 0 7521 1503 0

Contents

Foreword   iv

Summary   1

Introduction   7

1   **Setting the context: impairment and physical activity**   11
     1.1   Introduction   11
     1.2   Diversity within the sample   12
     1.3   Perceived restrictions on amount or type of activity   14
     1.4   Reinforcing factors   16
     1.5   Facilitators   17

2   **Beliefs about the role and importance of physical activity**   19
     2.1   Conceptualising physical activity   19
     2.2   Perceived importance of physical activity in general   20
     2.3   Beliefs about appropriate levels of physical activity   21
     2.4   Perceived importance of other health actions   23
     2.5   Sources of beliefs   24

3   **Motivation**   26
     3.1   Perceived benefits of physical activity which influence motivation   26
     3.2   Self-motivation   30
     3.3   Influence of others in affecting motivation   36

4   **Opportunity**   42
     4.1   Awareness and information   42
     4.2   Someone to go with   45
     4.3   Getting there   46
     4.4   Provision   46
     4.5   Time and money   50

5   **Suggestions for promotion and provision**   52
     5.1   Preferences and choices   52
     5.2   Access to venues and activities   56
     5.3   Information and promotional material   57

6   **Overview and recommendations**   61
     6.1   A need to promote information about physical activity   61
     6.2   Avenues for promotion   62
     6.3   Work with providers   63

Appendices   64
Appendix 1:   Sample profile   64

Appendix 2:   Details of research methodology   66

Appendix 3:   Fieldwork documents   69

Foreword

There has been very little research conducted among disabled people and even less work published specifically about disabled people and physical activity. Research was needed not only to strategically inform the *ACTIVE* for LIFE's programme of work, but also to provide information and guidance to health and leisure professionals.

The Health Education Authority's (HEA) steering group for disabled people was consulted on the type and nature of the proposed research. The steering group decided that the most useful approach would be to use qualitative methodology and conduct research with disabled people themselves. A study was commissioned to explore their attitudes, beliefs, motivations and barriers (both intrinsic and extrinsic) in relation to physical activity.

The research reflects the HEA's physical activity work with people with disabilities. Therefore it has not concentrated on one particular group of disabled people but has been designed to reflect a wide variety of disability types and characteristics. In-depth interviews and focus groups have been undertaken with disabled people across four disability groups: blind or visually impaired, deaf or hearing impaired, physically impaired and people with learning difficulties.

The report will be a valuable tool for all professionals promoting physical activity among disabled people.

Alana Diamond
Physical Activity Research Manager
Health Education Authority

Summary

Background

This qualitative research study focused on disabled people's beliefs, perceptions, attitudes, and experiences in relation to physical activity. It was undertaken for the Health Education Authority (HEA) by Social & Community Planning Research (SCPR), and took place in the autumn of 1998. Its purpose was to provide background information for the HEA's 'ACTIVE for LIFE' campaign which is targeting different population groups. It follows similar qualitative studies conducted in recent years with non-disabled people.

Four broad categories of disability were covered in the study, including: physical impairment, hearing impairment, visual impairment, and learning difficulties. Some respondents had more than one impairment type.

The results are based on 40 in-depth interviews and five focus groups with disabled people and on brief initial consultations with disability organisations. A further discussion with parents of adults with learning difficulties was also included.

Setting the context: impairment and physical activity

Disabled people are people first and foremost. The same range and variety in attitudes and abilities towards physical activity, related to personal and sociodemographic characteristics, is demonstrated in this study as in the other studies in this series. Factors such as age, gender, social background and life stage influence attitudes towards physical activity.

Effects of the impairment itself, however, can also have an impact on ability and attitudes regarding physical activity. This varies across the impairment categories in relation to the particular loss of function, and in relation to such factors as whether an individual has more than one impairment, the nature of its side effects, and whether the condition is stable or deteriorating. Past experiences in relation to the impairment can also be influential, such as whether it is congenital or acquired later in life, and acquired suddenly or gradually.

The effect of impairment on physical ability is also largely shaped (for some people) by levels of access.

Many disabled people are therefore restricted in either the *amount* or the *type* of physical activity that they can do, or both. Some who are severely restricted can feel reluctant to try, fearful of making the condition worse, or simply not know what is physically possible for them to do, especially where the level of their fitness is to some extent determined by their condition, or where suppleness or muscular strength are affected. Or, impairment may be used as an 'excuse' to avoid physical activity, alongside many other excuses quoted also by non-disabled people.

The restrictive effect of the impairment may be reinforced by such factors as ageing, frailty, fear of injury, and weight.

Some disabled people do more physical activity as a direct result of their condition, such as pushing a wheelchair, walking the dog (guide dog), or using sign language (a movement-based language).

Factors which facilitate involvement and minimise the effect of impairment, include adapted activities or equipment, and extra assistance.

Beliefs about the role and importance of physical activity

'Physical activity' was conceptualised in a variety of ways from sport to everyday actions such as walking, housework, or gardening. This variety in definition is the same as found in other studies.

In some cases, impairment affected perceptions of what constituted physical activity: for some respondents with severe physical impairment, for example, the act of moving around generally was counted as physical activity because of the effort required.

The positive role that physical activity played in relation to health was acknowledged. Some went so far as to say that physical activity might hold a greater importance for disabled people in order to enable them to cope better with the effects of disability. Such effects were noted both physically, in terms of strength and fitness, and mentally, and in terms of the social and psychological add-on benefits, for example in maintaining an independent lifestyle.

Although there was a belief that physical activity generally was beneficial for health, there was little awareness that specific guidelines existed regarding the necessary frequency and extent of physical activity. If known about, there was little knowledge of what the guidelines comprised. This lack of awareness appeared to contrast with the awareness found in other studies among non-disabled people, though a large-scale survey would be needed to confirm this apparent difference.

There was a feeling among some that universal prescriptions regarding physical activity levels were inappropriate for disabled people. This is in common with the attitudes of many older people, as expressed in the earlier research. Advice on an individual basis was preferable, taking into account such factors as age and impairment.

Other health actions, notably diet and not smoking, were also perceived as important. Diet was perhaps seen as more important than physical activity, though diet and physical activity, were sometimes seen as complementary, or as compensatory in relation to each other. The importance of sleep, rest, relaxation, fresh air and, importantly, keeping a positive attitude, were also mentioned. Drink or drugs were little mentioned.

Respondents were largely unable to identify sources of their beliefs/knowledge about the benefits of physical activity. When mentioned, however, the medical profession, especially GPs, were key sources of information, especially in relation to the particular condition/impairment. Physiotherapists and other fitness or disability professionals were also mentioned and, occasionally, friends or family.

For respondents with learning difficulties, talks from staff at day centres had been influential. There was little mention of the media, perhaps due to the way that standard media images are far removed from some disabled people's self-perception, and also to reduced access to the media for some, notably deaf and visually impaired people.

Motivation

The perceived benefits of physical activity, as influencing motivation to do it, spanned the psychological (enjoyment and a feeling of well-being) and the physical (health/fitness benefits). This was consistent across the impairment groups. It also echoes the findings of other studies.

Enjoyment of physical activity included not only a sense of well-being but also some noted additional benefits for disabled people. These included: a sense of achievement and satisfaction in overcoming limitations, self confidence, social benefits (including meeting other disabled people), overcoming isolation, getting out and about, stress relief and, in some activities, reducing differences with non-disabled people.

Health benefits were mentioned in a number of different ways: in relation to maintaining general health and fitness (especially where there were health problems or ageing); keeping the body toned, building up muscles, preventing stiffness; and helping to maintain physical independence and an active life. Weight control was a further aspect for some, whether for reasons of body image or the desire to prevent further health or injury problems.

Yet, despite awareness of benefits, some people showed little interest in physical activity, and did not perceive that, on balance, taking part was beneficial to them personally.

Motivation to do physical activity in some ways was also linked to impairment: because of the likely additional effort needed to overcome practical barriers, which can be thought by some to outweigh the perceived benefit; and because impairment may lead to lower levels of self-confidence.

Self-consciousness and low confidence levels put off some disabled people from doing physical activity at public facilities. They described feelings of being different as a disabled person, of not fitting in at a facility such as a gym, or of needing to ask for 'too much' help. Confidence had a huge impact on whether and where physical activity was done.

Differences in motivation, confidence and attitudes to physical activity at different life stages were noted. The critical transition on leaving school or college in either continuing or getting out of the habit of doing sport, and the slowing down due to age, were two such stages that have been noted in earlier studies with the general population. Periods following marriage breakdown, or the death of a spouse, were similarly significant. For some respondents who had become disabled, the role of rehabilitation since the onset of impairment was critical in affecting motivation. Additionally, the time after a period in hospital often resulted in losing a degree of fitness which could be hard to regain.

Several further influences were apparent on disabled people's attitudes or motivation to take part in physical activity. These included school experiences, support from, and influence of, family and friends (including, as in other studies, whether or not there was a dog in the household), the influence of disability sports groups, of day centres (for some people with learning difficulties), and contact with the medical profession.

School experiences could have a positive or negative effect, depending on the range of opportunities and activities offered and the extent of competitiveness or compulsion. Disabled respondents had been excluded from doing physical activity in some mainstream schools.

Family or friends were influential in triggering motivation and in the provision of practical assistance and moral support. This worked across generations in both directions, for example in the wish to be active, as a disabled parent, with active children, and in receiving encouragement from parents, as a disabled child. Having friends to do physical activity with was a major influence on participation in several cases.

Disability sports groups played a significant motivating role for some respondents. They could contribute to a positive sense of identity, as an active disabled person, as well as offer accessible opportunities for activities, facilities, specialist equipment, and contact with disabled sports specialists and disabled achievers. Some respondents, however, saw these groups as focusing on competitive sport and as such were put off from joining.

The role of the medical profession in several cases seemed to be restrictive. Advice from GPs or physiotherapists about the type or extent of physical activity that an individual could do was often not forthcoming, or was confusing and unhelpful, or led to anxiety about injury.

Opportunity

External influences that affected participation in physical activity essentially related to problems of access. This covered many dimensions including issues of information provision, someone to go with, extent of suitable provision, physical access, attitudes of others, time and money. A wide range was mentioned overall, due partly to the variety of impairment types covered in the study. Poor access determines the degree to which impairment will have an effect on what physical activities are possible. Where there is total access, some impairments will have no effect at all.

Access barriers appeared to feature far more in this study than in the earlier studies among non-disabled people.

Lack of information was a problem from two points of view. First, there was low awareness among some disabled people about the sort of activities that were feasible in relation to the specific nature of their impairment or disabling condition. Second, there was low awareness of suitable facilities or opportunities for doing physical activity, particularly of those that were physically accessible and welcoming. Active promotion of such information was felt to be poor.

The need to find 'someone to go with' presented a potential barrier in this study as in others among the general population. For some disabled people, however, it was all the more pertinent where there was a wish to be accompanied for physical assistance or for help with communication, as an interpreter, or a 'pair of eyes'. A preference to have someone to go with for moral support was also stated by some, as well as for social reasons and general enjoyment. Some disabled people preferred to take part in physical activity with people who had the same impairment, but had difficulty in finding someone who shared an enthusiasm for their preferred sport.

Access to and from venues for physical activity was also potentially problematic. This was raised in terms of travel and transport problems, for example difficulties in the use of public transport; and in a feeling of vulnerability, especially for travel at night.

There were thought to be fewer opportunities for disabled people to take part in physical activity in terms of the extent of facilities available, especially of provision that was locally based. Cuts in provision over recent years were noted, for example in opportunities for specialist disabled sport (e.g. for deaf people), or in sessions organised from local authority day centres (e.g. for people with learning difficulties).

Poor physical access at existing facilities also restricted opportunities for disabled people. This related either to the design of buildings, or to a lack of aids or adaptations to equipment that would make it useable. The need to check beforehand that extra assistance would be forthcoming added to the 'hassle' factor. Restricted times of access to some disabled people were also noted.

Attitudes of other people sometimes presented a barrier. This included attitudes of providers, at policy level, regarding the inclusion or exclusion of people who had particular impairments, or the restriction on when they could take part; and attitudes of staff at the facilities, due to a fear of and lack of understanding of the disability, or being too busy to help. Attitudes of the other users or participants towards disability and towards disabled people, or apprehension about what these might be, were also a cause of concern. Some people had an expectation of difficulties, based on negative experiences in everyday life, and this was a deterrent.

Lack of time was a barrier especially for those in employment or training, or for those who had caring responsibilities, such as mothers of young children. This was also found in earlier studies with non-disabled people. Some disabled people had other priorities for their time, such as a preference for socialising rather than physical activity. Some time constraints, however, were related to the impairment: due to reduced energy levels, for example, or longer travel times to reach the more limited number of accessible facilities, or the fact that the activity took longer, or the need to find someone to go with and at times that were mutually convenient.

Financial constraints, especially pertinent to those who were not in paid employment, were occasionally mentioned. There were also extra costs involved for some disabled people: of transport, such as taxi fares if public transport was inaccessible, or of long journeys to reach accessible facilities; of specialist adapted equipment; and of assistance.

Suggestions for promotion and provision

As with the population in general, there was a mix of views among respondents about the type of activity that they would choose to do, with some of their preferences being shaped by negative images of certain activities and by their perception of their own abilities.

There was also a range in preferences to do activity in either an individual or an organised setting and, where organised, whether this would be part of mainstream provision or as some type of separate provision. Separate provision ranged from doing activity as part of a disability sports group or organisation through having separate sessions for disabled people to settings where additional assistance was available. Reasons for preferring separate provision were both positive, that it was a way of providing a supportive environment and specialist equipment, and more negative, because of fear of injury or lack of self-confidence.

Access to facilities and activities was a critical factor for respondents in making physical activity easier to do. Access included the physical access to and within buildings, access to equipment and facilities, the role and attitude of staff, ease of communication, and availability of information about local accessible facilities.

On the whole, respondents felt there was a need for more awareness and promotion of physical activity among disabled people. Suggestions for promotion messages at a general level included the use of positive images of disabled people to encourage the take-up of physical activity.

The two main avenues of promotion suggested were, firstly, campaign material, at local and national levels, to raise awareness generally about the benefits of physical activity, and what exercise options are available. Respondents with visual impairments and hearing impairments sometimes suggested the need for material to be available in formats other than print, for example tape or video. Secondly, the medical profession, in particular GPs, physiotherapists and hospitals, were felt to have an important potential role for some disabled people in raising awareness and in developing individualised programmes.

Introduction

Background to the study

The physiological health benefits of regular moderate intensity physical activity are now well documented.[1] Physical activity can also play an important role in increasing people's confidence and self-esteem, and provide a means to socialise. Studies have identified disabled people as one group of the population who are more likely to have a low rate of participation in physical activity.[2]

Disabled people are a heterogeneous group for whom regular physical activity is of great importance but has received very little attention. In general, disabled people are less active and have lower work capacity than people without disabilities. An inactive lifestyle compounds the effects of the disability or impairment and this makes it a public health issue. Poor stamina, reduced muscle strength and limited flexibility restrict functional ability and, therefore, personal independence.

'*ACTIVE* for LIFE' is a three-year national campaign which is run by the Health Education Authority (HEA) and is designed to encourage more people in England to be more active, more often. The campaign was launched in March 1996 and in the first year targeted the general population. In the second and third years of the campaign the HEA is targeting specific population groups, including disabled people.

It is against this background that the HEA commissioned this qualitative study, which was conducted by Social & Community Planning Research (SCPR) in autumn 1998.

Scope and objectives of the research

The specific objectives of the study were to explore, among disabled people:

- what is known about physical activity and its link with health
- attitudes towards participation in physical activity
- barriers and motivators regarding physical activity
- ways of overcoming barriers.

[1]US Department of Health and Human Services (1996). *Physical Activity and Health: A Report of the Surgeon General*. Atlanta. GA: US Department of Health and Human Service, Centers for Disease Control and Prevention, National Center for Chronic Disease Prevention and Human Promotion.

[2]Heath, G. W. and Fentem, P. H. (1997) 'Physical Activity among Persons with Disabilities – a public health perspective'. *Exercise and Sports Science Reviews*.

Four broad categories of impairment were identified by the HEA for coverage in the study. They include people who have:

- physical impairments
- hearing impairments
- visual impairments
- learning difficulties.

It was recognised that these groups are not mutually exclusive and any individual respondent may have more than one impairment type.

The research design and methodology

The design consisted of two stages: a brief preliminary consultation with national disability organisations representing each impairment category, followed by 40 in-depth interviews and five focus groups with disabled people, with approximately equal numbers of people across the four impairment categories. An additional focus group was also carried out with parent carers of people with learning difficulties, to amplify the data in relation to this impairment group. Lower and upper age limits of 18 and 70 were set in order to focus on disabled people where age was not the main barrier to activity. Interviewing took place in different areas of England, to ensure a geographical spread.

The sample was selected to ensure diversity, with a focus more on inactive than active people. Checks were made to ensure a range of respondent characteristics in terms of sex, age, whether disabled from birth or later in life, and whether or not in paid employment. Within the broad impairment categories, respondents also represented a variety of nature and severity of impairment, including for example, wheelchair users and people not using wheelchairs, people who were profoundly deaf and people who were hard of hearing. Respondents with learning difficulties, however, were not so severely disabled as to prevent them taking part in the study.

As a qualitative study, the aim was to describe the range of attitudes, barriers and motivations and the factors behind them. Measurement of the prevalence of particular attitudes or behaviour is not possible in a qualitative study because the sample is not designed, in its scale or composition, to provide statistical conclusions. For the same reasons it is not possible from this small study to draw conclusions for any one impairment category.

Conduct of the study

In order to reflect the diversity of the disabled population, the research used a number of different recruitment methods. The majority of the respondents were recruited from private households in the local fieldwork areas. This was supplemented by recruitment through local and national disability organisations, day centres, and supported accommodation.

Interviewing proceeded around a topic guide, which was used as a broad framework to explore a range of issues. Interviews and group discussions were tape recorded and transcribed verbatim for analysis. Based on both the tape recordings and the verbatim transcripts, a detailed content analysis was undertaken. Analytical charts were constructed, summarising the beliefs, attitudes, behaviours and experiences of respondents in relation to each of the issues, identifying recurrent themes or patterns of association within the data. Such charts, together with illustrative material taken verbatim from the interviews, form the basis of this report.

The overall sample of respondents, of organisations consulted and further methodological details, including copies of all the fieldwork documents, can be found in Appendices 1 to 3.

This report

The evidence from the study shows many similarities in attitudes and behaviour within and between people in the broad impairment categories. In view of this and of the fact that some respondents had more than one category of impairment, the findings for each group have not been reported separately but have been integrated on a thematic basis, with key differences between categories described where appropriate.

The report is structured to reflect the different factors and processes involved in the decision whether or not to take part in physical activity.

Chapter 1 sets the context for the report with a discussion about the diversity of impairment categories and the effect that impairment has, or is perceived to have, on physical activity.

Chapter 2 describes how respondents think about physical activity and their levels of knowledge and awareness about the importance and health benefits of physical activity.

Chapter 3 focuses on intrinsic barriers, the motivating and de-motivating factors felt by respondents, including perceived and actual benefits, factors influencing self-motivation, and the influence of other people.

Chapter 4 looks at extrinsic barriers or the degree of opportunity to take part in physical activity as perceived by respondents – the provision of facilities, attitudes of providers, time and money.

Chapter 5 describes respondents' suggestions and preferences for provision and promotion of physical activity.

Chapter 6 gives recommendations for key development strategies arising out of the research findings.

The ways respondents expressed their views are demonstrated throughout the report by the use of verbatim quotations. These are shown in italics and are labelled with indicators of sex, age and impairment. If they were physically active – that is their level of activity appeared to meet the Department of Health recommended levels of activity of 30 minutes of moderate intensity physical activity, five or more times a week – this is also indicated.

We have used the terms 'disabled people' or 'people with an impairment or disabling condition' throughout the report as a description of the population group as a whole. Respondents are also sometimes described as a member of impairment-specific groups or sub-groups where this is relevant to a specific issue. The following descriptions are used:

- wheelchair users

- profoundly deaf – people with little or no hearing

- hearing impaired – people with some hearing

- BSL users – people who communicate through using British Sign Language

- blind – people with no, or very little, sight

- visually impaired – people with some sight

- people with learning difficulties

Where findings are reported by broad impairment group, respondents with more than one impairment category may be part of either, or both, groups, depending on the particular issue under discussion and the extent to which one impairment category may predominate. The number of respondents with more than one impairment category was too small to look at their attitudes and experiences separately.

Reference to other studies

Comparison is made throughout the report to attitudes and experiences of non-disabled people in relation to physical activity, as reported in 'other studies'. These refer to previous qualitative research studies in the HEA's Qualitative Physical Activity Research Series, which were conducted among non-disabled people in specific age groups:

> *Physical activity – 'what we think'*
> Qualitative research among women aged 16 to 24, HEA, 1998
>
> *Physical activity – 'at our age'*
> Qualitative research among people aged over the age of 50, HEA, 1997.

1 Setting the context: impairment and physical activity

1.1 Introduction

The study of physical activity is intrinsically linked to physical ability, and for disabled people as a group, this means that any loss of function arising from an impairment or disabling condition is very likely to have a direct impact, in some way, on the ability to participate in physical activity. This will clearly vary depending on a number of different factors, perhaps the most significant of which are the nature of the impairment and the nature of the physical and social environment in which someone lives. The second of these factors might include: the built environment, the transport system, income levels, employment opportunities, attitudes of others and social support.

The different impact of these two aspects, and the nature of the relationship between them, is the subject of much debate in the field of disability research; emphasis on the effect of impairment is described as the 'Medical Model' and an emphasis on the effect of the environment is described as the 'Social Model'. This report looks at the way in which respondents described the different effects, and explores the way in which the two factors can influence each other. This first chapter explores respondents' experiences and views about the effect of impairment, but is not based on any sort of medical assessment of people's ability. These findings are presented at an early stage, not because they are given any weight over and above the impact of environmental factors, but because they provide a better understanding of the diversity of the sample and therefore set the context for the rest of the report.

The impact of an individual's impairment or disabling condition on the type or amount of physical activity they can do varies hugely. The findings suggest that the overall impact is closely linked to, and affected by, a number of other personal and societal factors:

- levels of physical and communication *access*
  (including attitudes of others towards disabled people)
- *awareness* or advice about personal physical activity options
- personal *attitude* to, and experience of, physical activity
- *preferences* in relation to physical activity.

These other factors are explored in Chapters 2 to 5 of this report.

1.2 Diversity within the sample

The population of disabled people is a very heterogeneous group, in terms of type and effect of impairment, and also demographically. The sample for this small-scale study aimed to capture some of this diversity, so that there is, among other things, a range of age, sex, ethnicity, and social background represented. As other studies have shown, these characteristics can have an impact on people's attitudes and behaviour in relation to physical activity. Not surprisingly, findings also suggested that the influence of personal characteristics of disabled people sometimes reflect that of the general population, but can be overlaid by the effect of their impairment.

However, the disabled population also has a number of social characteristics which distinguish it from the general population, the most significant of which are the greater likelihood of not being in work and, on average, far lower financial resources than the general population. Impairment is known to also have an effect on costs of living, for example the extra expense of special transport, equipment or assistance.

Range in the category of impairment and its physiological effects

The range of conditions which respondents had are represented in Figure 1, and their effects, on daily living as well as on physical activity, are described below.

The use of equipment or aids enabled the effect of impairment to be reduced in some cases, for example, the use of a wheelchair, a hearing aid, or a guide dog.

Respondents were selected in order to 'fit' one of four impairment categories – physical, visual, hearing and learning. Of course, some respondents had more than one impairment or impairment category, and these sometimes had multiple effects. Some respondents also had side-effects caused by their main condition or by medication. An example, at the more extreme end, was a woman with severe asthma, controlled over a number of years by steroids, which had led to her developing brittle bones, glaucoma and a weight problem. Other side-effects of certain disabling conditions or medication included loss of balance, fatigue and drowsiness.

For some respondents the perceived effect of a physical impairment seemed to over-ride the effect of a sensory impairment. So, for example, the inability to ride a bicycle was described as being due to arthritic knees, rather than a visual impairment and the effect of a severe heart condition appeared much greater than the effect of hearing loss.

There was a very wide range of effect due to hearing impairment. Where respondents had some loss of hearing, but were able to counter this with the use of a hearing aid or by accurate lip-reading, the effect on their daily life appeared to be less than for other respondents. For respondents who were profoundly deaf, however, the use of a separate language in British Sign Language (BSL) (for some people their first and main language) meant that their experiences were in some ways quite distinct from the rest of the sample, including the other hearing impaired respondents.

Figure 1: Range of impairment categories included

- **Physical impairments**
  - cerebral palsy
  - paralysis of one or both legs
  - paralysis of body from chest down
  - restricted leg mobility, with stiffness or pain – range of causes and severity
  - restricted leg and arm mobility – range of causes and severity
  - asthma – of differing severity
  - conditions causing fatigue and/or fluctuation (among other things)
  - general frailty, including brittle bones*
  - angina*
  - high blood pressure*
  - epilepsy*

- **Visual impairments**
  - no sight
  - partial sight – range of effects

- **Hearing and communication impairments**
  - no hearing – BSL users
  - partial hearing – lip readers
              – not lip readers
  - speech impairment*

- **Learning difficulties****
  - mild to moderate
    (medical diagnoses not requested)

* Respondents were not selected on the basis of these particular impairments, which were additional to their 'main' impairment.
** All learning difficulties respondents were recruited through day centres.

Another feature of the diversity of the sample (and the disabled population) can be a difference in experience and attitudes based on the point in their life when they became disabled, especially the difference between being disabled from birth or childhood, compared to acquiring an impairment later in life. For some respondents their experiences appeared to be shaped by whether they attended special schools or not, the effect of parents' attitudes to disability, and the extent and type of contact with the medical profession. Whether impairment was sudden or gradual, and whether it was stable or deteriorating, seemed to have influence on respondents' experiences and attitudes. The sample is too small to explore any effect of these factors in depth.

Range in physical activity

Most of the respondents in the study were selected on the grounds of being relatively inactive at the time of the study. However, a number of respondents were none the less taking part in physical activity to a varying degree. There was a range of activity types, although respondents were, on the whole, taking part in the more common types of activity – swimming, gyms, exercise classes, cycling, gardening, football – as well as walking the dog.

1.3   Perceived restrictions on amount or type of activity

Possible options for physical activity

For some respondents, impairment contributed to a disincentive to try activities that were felt to be impossible or difficult, whereas others' disinclination was based on experience: they had tried a particular activity and found themselves unable physically to do it.

The extent to which respondents are aware of what they can or cannot do physically is therefore a critical issue:

> *There are a lot of people need to be educated into dividing what they really can't do, like I'd never be able to do pole vault or the long jump or anything like that, it's physically impossible, but that doesn't mean I can't do any activity at all. There is a dividing line and some people need to be educated into where is that line, what can I do, what can't I do.*   Male, 24, spina bifida, wheelchair user

This issue is explored further in Chapter 4.

Across all impairment groups, there were some respondents who had the attitude towards physical activity that 'you can do anything you want'; their impairment did not restrict in any way their ability to do physical activity, (although it might require different ways to do it):

> *I'm just normal. I'm equal of hearing people, there's nothing there to stop me.*   Male, 46, profoundly deaf since early childhood

However, this view was rare, and most respondents felt either that their impairment restricted the *amount* of activity they could do or that there were some particular *types* of activities that were either impossible, or more difficult, because of their impairment.

At the same time, a few respondents said that they felt they sometimes used their impairment as an excuse for not doing activities.

> *I said I'm not going because I would just be conscious that I couldn't do it. He said the only reason you can't do it is because you're overweight, I said, 'No it isn't, I'm blind as well.' I've got another excuse.*
> Female, 42, visual impairment since age 16

Impairment may also sometimes have an opposite effect of resulting directly in *more* physical activity, for example, having to walk a guide dog every day, using sign language (as a movement-based language), or having to walk from place to place because of not being able to drive.

'There's nothing really that's possible'

Respondents varied greatly in the extent to which they perceived their physical ability to be restricted by their impairment or disabling condition. For some respondents, the two were very closely interconnected – the level of their *fitness* was, to some extent, determined by their condition, especially conditions such as asthma or angina which are related to heart or lung capacity.

Similarly, the extent of a respondent's suppleness or muscular strength could be determined in part by particular types of degenerative diseases, such as multiple sclerosis or arthritis. The effects of certain conditions such as severe pain or fatigue and the unpredictability of some conditions also resulted in respondents having a greater physical restriction. For respondents with these impairments, their perception was that the amount of activity they could do was directly and severely restricted by their impairment. It was very difficult for some of them to think about any physical activity which they would actually be able to do.

I can do some, but it's a case of take it gently because otherwise it brings an attack on and the attacks wipe you out ... It wipes you out for the rest of the day. So I know to take it steady ... There's nothing really that's possible for me.
Female, 42, multiple sclerosis, wheelchair user

I want to do it, I'd love to do it, but I know I can't, so what's the point ... I have tried.
Female, 33, spinal injury causing restricted mobility and severe pain

I can walk from here to the toilet, the toilet's only down here. On a good day I can walk to the kitchen, but then I can't walk back, I have to sit in there to get my breath back. I've got the settee there so I will sit there and then come back over here.
Female, 50, severe asthma

Well, I think my health's against me ... I've got angina, I suffer with asthma, on tablets for funny breathing, so I don't rush about.
Male, 52, angina, hearing impairment

General restrictions on activity were sometimes anticipated and were sometimes based on direct experience. One woman with a spinal injury which caused severe pain and restricted mobility said she had tried a whole range of different activities (actually against medical advice) but that any physical activity at all was very painful, and afterwards she was sometimes unable to move for several days. On the whole this group of respondents referred to their ability to do physical activity or movement in its widest sense when they were talking about the effect of their impairment (this is amplified in Chapter 2 in a discussion on conceptualising physical activity).

Restrictions to certain types of activity

Impairments which affect mobility, sight and hearing can have an effect on the *type* of physical activity that can be done. How much effect respondents thought it had depended partly on the nature and severity of the impairment. At the same time, among respondents with similar impairments, there were different expectations and experiences, suggesting that impairment is just one of a number of factors which interact to cause the overall impact.

Restrictions varied for each of the impairment groups. Respondents with total or partial loss of sight tended to name particular sports or activities which they were unable to do because of their lack of sight. This included cycling (except on a tandem), ball games, and, for one respondent, sailing. Some visually impaired respondents made a distinction between 'fast' ball games (for example squash, badminton, tennis) and slower ones which were perceived to be possible when adapted, for example cricket, bowls, snooker and football.

Both visually and hearing impaired respondents talked about finding it difficult to follow a class instructor, where the movements are both demonstrated visually, and with an oral commentary. Some deaf respondents noted that dancing or aerobics could only be done on the type of floor which enabled the sound vibrations to be felt. Swimming was not possible for respondents who had certain ear conditions and had to avoid getting water in their ears; one respondent with a hearing impairment was also concerned about further injuring the ear if taking part in vigorous team activity.

Among physically impaired respondents, the extent of impairment had a direct effect on the type of activity, as well as the amount. One female wheelchair user was very motivated and active in a number of different physical activities, but had found that her impairment made it impossible for her to play tennis.

For people with learning difficulties there can be problems taking part in activities where intellectual functioning affects physical ability. This can apply to some team sports, for example where there is a need to understand specific rules or tactics. However, the central issue for this impairment category is the need to provide motivation and support to facilitate participation in physical activity.

1.4 Reinforcing factors

The effect of impairment for any individual is not constant, and will shift in relation to the state and nature of the condition itself, as well as the person's circumstances. A number of factors which are closely related to impairment add to, and reinforce, the effect of impairment. Particularly significant among these appeared to be: ageing, frailty and fear of injury, and weight.

Ageing

Age and disability seemed to be connected in a complex way. Some older respondents in the sample had acquired a disability later in life, and some had grown older with a condition they had had much of their life. In both scenarios, there appeared to be an effect of 'slowing down', which meant that the role of their impairment was sometimes difficult to separate from the effect of their ageing.

> *I'm not real energetic no more. If I was younger, but I'm not energetic now, just take life as it comes.* Male, 52, angina, hearing impairment

Ageing can also bring with it increased frailty, loss of muscle strength, and increased risk or anxiety about certain impairments, such as heart conditions.

As with the population in general, ageing affects disabled people in different ways, some of which may be related to their impairment. Several respondents seemed to have the behaviour and attitudes of 'older' people even though they were not old.

Frailty and concern about injury

Across all impairment categories, there was a concern or fear of causing further injury or damage to an existing condition, or of bringing on an acute episode, for example asthma, angina or epileptic attack. This seemed to lie behind some respondents' belief that they could not do physical activity. This resulted in not taking part in any vigorous or strenuous activity, although they were comfortable with the idea of light or gentle physical activity. For others, there was a concern about almost any kind of activity – because of pain at the time, and the after effect.

I've got to restrain myself. Like I go swimming and I can go without the board, but I'm scared just in case I lose balance then it can affect my eye ... Because I have a mishap then I could break my fall or have damage to my eye, which I only have one eye.

Female, 58, visual impairment and restricted mobility

As I say if it wasn't for that I think I'd be 100% fit, put it that way. But you see with this being like this I can't walk far because I'm frightened of going over. Male, 69, hearing impairment affecting sense of balance

I've got physiotherapy activities that I'm supposed to do to aid me with my walking and to aid my condition. But I've had to pack that in because they've discovered I've got angina and the more I do it the more angina attacks I have. So I now have to be very, very careful, which I was most disappointed about. Female, 42, multiple sclerosis, wheelchair user

Well over-tiredness can bring epilepsy on ... Also if you do vigorous exercise you've got to be careful with your back again as well. You've got to be careful what sorts of exercises you do ... I can do most things, but very light exercises. Sports-wise, things like that, that's out really.
Male, 42, no use in one leg following accident, pain, uses wheelchair part-time

Anxiety about injury led to some respondents wanting supervision while doing activity, or medical advice, to be sure that they were not overdoing it (see Chapter 4).

There was also an additional element of impairment-related safety for some blind respondents, in relation to fear of traffic, or of colliding with other people, for example in a swimming pool, or on a football pitch.

Some respondents had been given medical advice to refrain from, or restrict the amount or type of activity they should do because of their impairment.

Weight

Being overweight can add to any existing mobility restrictions, as well as possibly causing strain on the heart, and high blood pressure. There were a small number of respondents with severe weight problems, and their responses suggested that their perception of what they were physically able to do was affected by their weight as well as their impairment.

1.5   Facilitators

Impairment appeared to have the least effect on respondents' ability to take part in physical activity where they were involved in sports or activities which were either adapted in some way or used special equipment, or assistance. The role of access to facilities is discussed in Chapter 5, but is included here as a demonstration of how adaptations had removed the effect of impairment for some respondents who were physically active.

Adapted activities or equipment

For some visually impaired respondents, this meant playing cricket or other ball games with a ball that made a noise. Respondents who were wheelchair users also took, or had taken, part in wheelchair sports, for example wheelchair rugby, hand-cycling, or wheelchair athletics. Archery was also given as an example of a sport which could be easily adapted, if required, so that wheelchair users could compete on an equal basis with others.

For profoundly deaf respondents who used BSL, the equivalent of 'adapted activities' was perhaps a sport or activity where all the players are deaf. This overcomes the difficulty of communication between deaf and hearing team players.

However, some respondents were not keen on the idea of special or segregated provision (this is discussed in Chapter 5). Others did not appear to have any knowledge about the options for adapted activities. Taking part in adapted or special activities is obviously dependent on there being available opportunities or facilities.

Extra assistance

Specific assistance was felt to minimise the effect of impairment. This ranged from assistance during the activity itself, for example, help with positioning while playing snooker or bowls for visually impaired people, or assistance at the start of an activity, such as being helped in and out of a swimming pool, or a canoe. Another way in which extra help had facilitated respondents to take part in activity was having initial one-to-one tuition where learning is otherwise predominantly based on observation.

The need for assistance in getting to, or taking part in, sport was a major factor for some respondents, (this is discussed in Chapter 4). The extent to which respondents felt they needed assistance appeared to be partly related to the severity of their impairment, but also to the extent to which they sought to be independent. In addition, some respondents felt very uncomfortable about relying on other people for help and assistance, whereas others who viewed it as 'facilitation' were more comfortable with the idea.

Having special equipment, personal assistance or taking part in adapted activities are all ways of enabling independence and full participation for some groups of disabled people. However, this type of facilitation is possibly more suited to some impairments than others. It could be that impairments or disabling conditions which have a direct effect on the amount of activity that can be done do not benefit in the same way from the provision of equipment or assistance.

2 *Beliefs about the role and importance of physical activity*

This chapter describes the general attitudes to, and beliefs about, physical activity that were expressed throughout the study. Along with Chapter 1, it helps to set the context for the discussion of barriers and motivating factors towards participation in physical activity discussed in later chapters. Beliefs that specifically motivate participation in physical activity are discussed further in Chapter 3.

Perhaps because of the demographically diverse nature of this sample, there was little in the way of main themes or patterns emerging around beliefs about physical activity. Personal characteristics (such as age, sex and social background) appeared to shape beliefs as much as, if not more than, the fact of having an impairment. However, the way in which disabled people thought about physical activity and its role in their life (see section 2.1) may, in part, be shaped by their impairment and perception of their physical ability.

2.1 Conceptualising physical activity

There were very varying views about what might constitute 'physical activity'. Definitions ranged from a relatively narrow idea, in terms solely of traditional 'sports', to a far broader view, which included general day-to-day activities, such as walking, housework or gardening. Some respondents considered that any moving around or getting out and about was physical activity. This distinction between thinking of physical activity as a separate activity or as incorporated in daily life has also been found in other studies.

For some respondents, impairment did not have any effect on their image of what constitutes physical activity. Yet for others, the fact that they were disabled had influenced this perception in a number of ways. Firstly, the idea of physical activity was linked to their sense of personal physical restriction, so that moving around generally was not taken for granted as it is by the rest of the population; physical activity perceived to be an integral part of their life.

> *Generally speaking, everything really that we have to do [is physical activity]. You're always pushing your chair, you never get away from pushing your chair, work's a lot of physical activity and getting to work really ... Getting in and out of the bath, funnily enough, which to an able-bodied person would seem nothing, but you literally have to push yourself up so it is actually a lot more physical than it looks.*

Female, 22, no use of legs, wheelchair user

There were different opinions about the extent to which work should be counted as a physical activity if it involved *more* physical effort because of an impairment. For some disabled people, it was '*just part of everyday life*'.

This effect of impairment on concepts of physical activity was also illustrated where respondents' perceptions had shifted following the onset of impairment or the deterioration of a disabling condition. Housework, for example, was something that some respondents had then begun to see as a physical activity:

> *Very much so, at the moment, yeah. At one time it [housework], was a doddle, but because of health problems now I find it difficult.*
>
> Female, 40s, visual impairment, and debilitating illness

Another way in which respondents' definitions of physical activity were shaped by their experience of impairment was that they included activities additional to the more standard range described in other studies. These were activities that were specific to, and in some cases necessitated by, their impairment. For example:

- building of arm and upper body strength where there is no use of the legs
- regular walking of guide dog
- use of vigorous sign language.

Some respondents made a distinction between a general view of what constitutes physical activity, and a different (restricted) view about what they were physically able to do. So, for example, a wheelchair user made a distinction between walking, for the general population, and pushing her wheelchair for her. This seemed to be based on a perception of 'difference' from other people:

> *It's very hard, you don't actually realise until you actually have to think about it, like just now ... about what exercise able-bodied people do ... Although one of the things we always say is we like to be as much like able-bodied people as possible, there are certain things that are always going to be different.*
>
> Female, 22, no use of legs, wheelchair user

> *Well me personally, I know that I'm limited. So I think you haven't really got a lot of choice, because you have got limitations.*
>
> Female, 45, blind from birth, active

Other respondents' definitions of what constituted physical activity were more general and not related to their personal situation. They rejected the idea of activities that they felt were aimed – or even pushed – at them as disabled people. For example, some blind respondents rejected the idea of blind sports like bowls, which they also felt had an older people's image.

There appeared to be some differences between older and younger respondents' perceptions of physical activity. For example, it seemed that younger respondents' images were more 'sports' oriented, whereas older respondents included more of the day-to-day activities. However, this might also have been related to different effects of impairment among older respondents.

2.2   Perceived importance of physical activity in general

There was a general belief among respondents in the importance of some sort of physical activity, and its *equal* importance for disabled people. There was also, for some, a belief in the *particular* importance for disabled people to take part in physical activity in order to cope better with disability, both physically (in terms of strength and fitness) and mentally:

> *[It's important] just for everyday living really. If for some reason I couldn't push my chair then everyday activities around the house like making my dinner and cups of tea, even a daft thing like answering the phone ... Getting on and off the bed and the settee, that takes a lot of effort.*
>
> Female, 22, no use of legs, wheelchair user

There was a difference in emphasis about the extent to which physical activity was *needed* for health or fitness reasons and whether its value came from add-on psychological and social benefits. There was also a strong sense of the importance of physical activity in maintaining an independent lifestyle, or 'keeping going'. This included both physical and mental elements (discussed in Chapter 4).

Perceived health benefits of physical activity

On the whole, respondents did not have much objective knowledge about the general health benefits of physical activity. Their beliefs about the need for physical activity appeared to be grounded in their own circumstances and condition. Where people felt there were health or fitness benefits of physical activity, therefore, this was reactive to their perception of their own condition – for example, being aware of a slowing down, or getting aches and pains, or wishing to lose weight, or improve circulation.

Some respondents talked about physical activity being important in order to stay fit, prevent physical decline on ageing, and keep healthy. This was talked about in very general terms. However, other respondents mentioned specific effects of physical activity such as suppleness, muscle-building and keeping their bodies toned. Not losing breath, body systems working and better circulation were also commented on.

Although some older respondents perceived an increased health need for physical activity, this sometimes went hand-in-hand with feeling a need to '*slow down*', as a result of either ageing or deteriorating health.

The specific benefits of physical activity, including health benefits, that influenced motivation to participate are discussed in Chapter 3.

2.3 Beliefs about appropriate levels of physical activity

Respondents' beliefs about whether they did enough activity, and how much they should do, were shaped by two main factors:

- their perception of own fitness level
- their knowledge or beliefs about appropriate levels of physical activity.

Perception of own fitness and activity level

The amount of physical activity that respondents were doing did not necessarily coincide with their perception of their own fitness. On the whole 'inactive' respondents perceived themselves to be relatively unfit, particularly if they had done more physical activity in the past. However, some respondents who would be assessed as inactive by Department of Health measures, felt that their fitness was good or average.

Some expressed uncertainty about how they would know whether they were fit or not, and how they would know whether they were doing 'enough' physical activity. Others measured their fitness in terms of more absolute physical terms, for example, getting out of breath running for the bus or feeling the after-effects of physical activity:

> *I feel fit, but I'm not physically fit. I wouldn't say I was physically fit. If you said to me do a day's work I probably couldn't, because the next day I would be covered in aches and pains and that's when you could tell me straight away that I wasn't fit.* Male, 53, visual impairment in recent years

Respondents assessed how fit they were and how fit they should be in terms of different measures:

- Being 'fit enough'

this included, for example, feeling sufficiently independent to deal with the needs of their day-to-day life (especially wheelchair users) and parents, particularly mothers, needing to keep up with children.

> *As long as I'm fit enough to take care of myself personally, like move round with the chair, manoeuvre myself in and out of my car and other places then really as long as I can do that with no problems I think that's sufficient.* Male, 24, no use of legs, wheelchair user

- Their relative fitness

respondents compared their current level of fitness with past levels and against other people's fitness – sometimes those with a similar condition or age to them and sometimes not. For example, one very inactive woman, whose condition made it very difficult for her to do much activity at all, none the less felt that she was active in relation to others:

> *[State of health?] Sort of middling, in between. I am fairly healthy to how other people are with MS, I am more active than most MS sufferers.* Female, 42, multiple sclerosis, wheelchair user

The effect of these factors on people's perceptions mean that where some respondents saw themselves as being as fit as when they were younger, or as fit as they needed to be, or as fit as others their age, their perceived need for physical activity was less.

Low awareness of specific physical activity prescriptions

Awareness of the health benefits of physical activity tended to be only in general terms. There was little awareness of the significance of levels of physical activity and hardly any knowledge that specific guidelines existed regarding the necessary frequency and extent of physical activity that was beneficial to health. If known about, there was little knowledge of what the guidelines comprised.

This lack of awareness appeared to contrast with other studies in this series, among non-disabled people. It may be due to the lesser exposure to media messages for some disabled people, such as those who are visually or hearing impaired. A large-scale survey would be needed, however, to confirm this apparent difference.

As well as a lack of awareness of Department of Health guidelines, there was also an element of confusion in interpreting them. This was noted in responses to the guidelines when explained during the interview. The element that seemed to be the least understood was the degree of intensity. '*What is brisk walking?*', '*What is heavy housework?*' were the type of queries expressed. Interestingly, some respondents who were doing very little in the way of appropriate activity, none the less said that the recommendation seemed like a 'sensible' amount. This may have been thinking the amount sensible for other people, the general population, but not for them. For other respondents, the confusion arose from interpreting their activity, for example, believing that light housework meant that they were meeting the recommended amount. Needing to get out of breath did not seem to fit in with some respondents' understanding of physical activity (see section 2.1). Because people with impairments and the rest of the population have different physical abilities, it may be that there should be alternative measures of activity or fitness.

Perhaps because of a lack of knowledge about how much physical activity is recommended for people in general, beliefs about the appropriate amount of physical activity appeared to be determined more by a number of personal factors, for example, age and degree of impairment. These factors influenced views of how much activity can be done, and how much should be done, sometimes leading to a belief in the need for different activity or fitness standards. This was especially true where the disabling condition is, or results in, pain, fatigue, heart conditions, or asthma. This was based on a fear or anxiety about making conditions worse (see Chapter 1). There was some belief that general prescriptions should be different depending on age, with older people not being expected to do so much. This echoes the attitudes of older people in general, as described in earlier research.

Some respondents felt strongly that it was up to each individual, in other words what someone is able to do, or of what they might want to do.

2.4   Perceived importance of other health actions

There was a fairly low awareness of the health benefits of other actions. Diet was regarded as important in combination with physical activity by some respondents, while others thought it more important, and some as less important. Another view was to see diet as critical for health but not necessarily for fitness.

Diet was also seen as an alternative to physical activity for some respondents when physical activity was felt to be difficult or impossible. Diet and physical activity were also seen as complementary or compensatory to each other:

If you're eating loads of junk food I think you should exercise more because it's bad for you.

Female, 20, visual impairment in recent years, active

> *Personally, I would like to see the two go together. But as I get older I most probably would lay off sport a bit, so I would be looking to eating sensibly, try and eat the right foods. But at the moment for me, at a certain age, I think the two go together.*   Male, 37, profoundly deaf, active

The importance of diet was seen as being to control both weight and certain conditions, such as high blood pressure, diabetes or high cholesterol. On the whole, respondents talked about a good diet in general terms, but some mentioned particular elements, for example avoiding fatty foods, chocolate or sugar, and eating fruit, vegetables or salads.

Respondents generally had an awareness of smoking as being unhealthy, although this did not necessarily influence their action. There were a number of smokers among the sample, some of whom said that they smoked through stress or boredom, which was linked to the effect of their impairment.

Other health actions were occasionally mentioned which were more related to a general sense of well-being. These included sleep, rest, relaxation and fresh air. Maintaining a positive attitude was also seen as related to keeping healthy:

> *If I'm happy, life goes OK, and I'm healthier.*
> Male, 23, profoundly deaf since early childhood

Drink or drugs were little mentioned.

2.5   Sources of beliefs

Presumably as a result of generally low levels of awareness, respondents were largely unable to identify particular sources of knowledge about physical activity.

The medical profession and, in particular, GPs appeared to be one of the main sources of knowledge and influence. This was normally in relation to the respondent's particular condition, having been given medical advice to increase or reduce their amount of activity rather than about physical activity levels more generally. Respondents who had not spoken to their GP about physical activity none the less mentioned the GP as the main person who would influence them if they were to listen to anyone. In addition to GPs and physiotherapists, other fitness or disability professionals were sometimes quoted as sources of beliefs. There was a feeling that GPs or hospital doctors were the only ones playing this role:

> *I think really you are only encouraged if there's something wrong in the beginning. A lot of people have done it through the doctor or maybe the hospital. You've gone for some reason and they say, 'Oh well exercise will improve it'.*   Female, 53, hearing impairment, asthma and back pain, active

For respondents with learning difficulties, talks from day centre staff appeared to have been influential as a source of information.

Friends and family were occasionally an important source of views about how much physical activity should be done.

The media appeared to play a small role, especially television. A small number of respondents referred to *Mr Motivator*, in particular to some chair exercises that had been demonstrated on the programme, which had been received very positively. It may be that standard images of physical activity promoted in the media are fairly far removed from disabled people's self-perception, and they do not identify with such images.

In addition, deaf people and visually impaired people have less access to standard media formats, so they are unlikely to be good sources of knowledge and information.

3 *Motivation*

Chapters 3 and 4 describe the range of factors that were shown to encourage and discourage respondents to do physical activity. This chapter focuses more on the motivational, or intrinsic, factors, while the emphasis of Chapter 4 is more on extrinsic barriers – those that influence opportunity.

Respondents' motivation to do exercise or physical activity was largely shaped by three separate areas which form the structure of this chapter:

- perceived benefits of doing physical activity (the anticipated or experienced) (3.1)

- self-motivation, level of confidence and determination (3.2)

- the influence of other people (3.3).

These factors could exert either a positive or a negative influence on individual motivation, and could change at different times of life. Throughout this chapter, therefore, the range of intrinsic barriers, as well as motivators, with regard to take-up of physical activity becomes apparent.

3.1 Perceived benefits of physical activity which influence motivation

As shown in Chapter 2 (section 2.2), most respondents believed in the general value and importance of physical activity. Yet, despite this, some showed little interest in physical activity, and did not perceive there to be any particular benefits to them personally in taking part.

> *I'm just happy as I am, just set in my own ways now … I'm not really bothered.*
> Male, 52, hearing impairment

> *I don't know whether I'm bothered now … If I was getting fatter I would make sure I did it.*
> Male, 69, hearing impairment

Among respondents who were interested in doing physical activity to some extent, there was a wide range of perceived benefits, and a wide variation in the apparent influence of these benefits. For some, the benefits were a major motivating factor; for others, they were more a perceived advantage, but one which was easily over-ridden by barriers (such as the extent of impairment, or lack of self-confidence, lack of provision, etc.). The range of benefits of physical activity that were mentioned overall was based both on direct experience and on expectation.

There was a fairly high level of consistency across impairment groups in terms of the major perceived benefits of physical activity. These were described in terms of two broad areas: enjoyment or well-being, and health and fitness.

It should be noted that the order of the points in Figure 2 does not indicate order of emphasis.

Figure 2: Benefits of physical activity influencing motivation

> ***The range of factors mentioned:***
>
> **Psychological: enjoyment and well-being**
> - enjoyment, fun or sense of well-being
> - achievement, overcoming limitations, seeing results
> - self-confidence, self-worth
> - reduce differences with non-disabled population [some activities], freedom, independence
> - social benefit, with friends/make new friends, overcoming isolation, getting out and about
> - stress-relief
>
> **Physical: health and fitness**
> - general health and fitness
> - building muscles, preventing stiffness, keep body toned
> - weight control
> - self-reliance, maintain active life and independence
> - preventing future illness/injury

Sometimes these factors were perceived as quite distinct from each other and the enjoyment, or feel-good factor, was very consciously placed above any fitness benefits of physical activity. For some respondents, expecting that physical activity was *not* going to be enjoyable or satisfying, was the reason for their lack of interest:

> *I think it's too much like hard work, and really not what I want to do ...*
> *I work hard at work, in my time I want some enjoyment.*
>
> Male, 31, cerebral palsy, wheelchair-user

> *If I was being persuaded to do something on the grounds of the other advantages that I might gain and then find out that it would also do something for my health as an afterthought, then maybe it would be something I would take notice of.*   Male, 27, totally blind from birth

For other respondents, the health or fitness element was the primary and underlying reason to do activity, but a desire for fun or a social element was the *motivating factor* or immediate reason that could trigger them into doing it:

> *I've got a weight problem and I do need the exercise ... [but] if it's deadly serious and mundane I'm not motivated to want to do it. I like that idea of having a bit of fun, a bit of repartee.*   Female, 42, partially sighted, who
> has progressively lost sight since age 16

Mental or social benefits

A high value tended to be placed on the capacity of physical activity to create a sense of psychological well-being in general. This included a sense of independence, of freedom, of self-confidence or self-worth, relief of stress, and also the ability to reduce differences with the rest of the population and feel less disabled when doing particular exercises or sports.

As far as I'm concerned, I'm as able bodied as anybody else in the water
Male, 42, restricted use of legs since accident, wheelchair user

A related value across all impairment groups was having a sense of achievement or satisfaction; for some this took the form of a general attitude to life, but was also shaped by living with an impairment and seeing physical activity as a way of overcoming limitations or restrictions. Other respondents regarded physical activity as a demonstration of a determination not to give in, for example in the face of physical impairment.

I suppose the feeling that you've actually achieved being able to do something. When I was young you've got that many people telling you that you're disabled, you can't do this, you can't do that, so to actually go to somebody and take say a medal or a trophy up to them and say look I've done this, I've won this, was just a feeling of achievement really.
Female, 22, leg and back problems, wheelchair user

I don't want to be bedridden; bed's the last place I want to be.
Male, 65, restricted mobility since road traffic accident

For some visually impaired people, the ability to take part in something which did not rely on being able to see for its sense of satisfaction or enjoyment was important.

Because I can spend enough time on my own and being out with your dog walking, when you don't see what's going on around you, there's no visual stimulation. Unless you've got a packet of sweets in your pocket there's not much more! ... If you [sighted interviewer] were out for a walk somewhere you are very aware of what's happening around you, people's facial expressions, they'll smile, you'll smile back, somebody will go past in a car and put their hand up. If you're out as a blind person with a guide dog, you're just walking. You might as well be just anywhere, there's no motivation to do it.
Female, 42, partially sighted, who has progressively lost sight since age 16

Across impairment groups, the social element of doing physical activity was also highly valued. The benefits came from doing physical activity with existing friends, as well as using physical activity as an opportunity to make new friends. Where respondents did not place a high value on the social element of physical activity, this was sometimes connected to a low level of self-confidence, which was shaped by their experience of negative attitudes from other people (discussed in Chapter 4).

I don't talk to anybody ... I feel better when I just keep myself to myself.
Female, 33, hearing impairment

*People can be so nasty, but animals love you to bits ... I love animals
and I love doing things by myself and I love trying to achieve by myself.
I'm not a people person.*   Female, late-40s, partially sighted

The value placed on social benefits may also reflect respondents' feelings of
isolation or their difficulties living in a society which, in many ways, does little to
accommodate disability. Deaf respondents (who used BSL) sometimes placed a
particularly high value on doing physical activity with other deaf people. This was
driven by a social need, caused by the difficulty of relaxing in a hearing world that
made communicating a stressful experience for them.

*Well I think it's part of deaf culture, it's a way of building friendships so
you can play against other clubs, other teams around Britain and as you
know the deaf community is a very small community ... It's a way of
maintaining contact with all the other deaf people and I think that's why
it's so important.*   Male, 37, deaf from birth, active

The belief in this as a major motivating factor for deaf people made one respondent
suggest that, with the introduction of more advanced telecommunication systems
deaf people were now starting to take less part in clubs and sports because their
need for communication was not so great.

Respondents who were otherwise quite isolated also saw physical activity as a way
of doing something, or of just going out:

*You meet people and it gets you out of the house because if you live within
four walls I think mentally you will feel sick.*   Female, 58, partially sighted,
some restricted mobility since accident

Health and fitness benefits

The two main areas of health or fitness benefits which appeared to act as
motivating factors were:

- the wish to stay healthy or active, especially where there was an
  awareness of health problems or ageing

- the wish to keep the body toned; or to lose (or control) weight.

The benefits of physical activity in maintaining an active life, and not 'stagnating',
were mentioned by the older or the more severely disabled respondents.

*It'll give me my energy back. If you stop doing things your energy levels go
down to nothing, but once you start getting back into the swing your
energy levels, it sounds daft, because you're doing more, it goes up. I'm
well aware of that and I want my energy levels to go back up.*   Female, 40s,
partially-sighted from birth, long-term illness and arthritis

Building up muscles, or preventing stiffness, as well as maintaining fitness, were
also seen as important benefits in order to maintain a more independent life. One
young wheelchair user was consciously exercising since she had started living
independently on her own, as an aspect of maintaining her independence:

It made me think you've got to be able to do it now, you've got to be able to. Not that I am totally on my own because we have carers that live on site ... But if anything ever happened and for some reason ... we needed to get somewhere to help them or get someone to help them, then you need to physically be able to get out and do it. So I suppose it's the security now, the more I know I can do, the safer I know I am really.

Female, 22, leg and back problems, wheelchair user

It stops me getting any more stiff than I am. As I say, I think if you don't do these things, if your bones get set I suppose or whatever they do, then they're going to get worse instead of better, they are going to lie dormant.

Female, 68, physical and visual impairment since accident

For some respondents, keeping going meant needing to see results even when there was a fairly strong health or fitness motivation. One woman, who was otherwise fairly determined to do some activity and not 'give in', was taught gentle upper body exercises by her nurse, but abandoned them because she felt that they had not worked.

Weight control was also recognised as a benefit of physical activity for respondents who wanted to keep their weight or body fat under control, and for those who were overweight and wanted to lose weight. Sometimes the wish to control weight was motivated by body image, at other times by a desire to prevent further health or injury problems:

I just want to get some weight off so that I don't put pressure on my leg, that's all I'm scared of is the weight.
Female, 33, physical disability
since accident

I'm very aware of things like breast cancer and stuff like that and the fact that if you're obese you're much more likely to get stuff like that.
Female, 42, partially sighted, who has progressively lost sight since age 16

3.2   Self-motivation

Despite being aware of the value and benefits of physical activity, some respondents were not sufficiently motivated to actually do any, or an increased amount of, physical activity. Self-motivation was clearly linked to impairment and disability in a number of ways. The study demonstrated ways by which:

- impairment and disability may make the additional effort outweigh the perceived benefit, requiring increased determination

- impairment may lead to lower levels of self-confidence.

Figure 3: Self-motivation

The range of factors mentioned

Determination

- to overcome additional barriers, related to disability
- the barriers can make you feel worse, need to be more determined
- overcoming apathy of 'is it worth it?'

  but also

- not giving in
- challenging expectations

Confidence

- lack of support
- low confidence/self esteem
- restricting ability to go out
- feeling different/embarrassed
- dark/security/safety

Levels of determination

It was generally felt that the effect of impairment and of a disabling society meant that it was harder for disabled people to take part in physical activity. Rather than enjoying the experience, therefore, the practice of physical activity could become a matter of 'survival', because of the extra effort needed in the face of practical barriers. This was perceived as a discouraging factor, and mentioned by respondents both in relation to other disabled people and to themselves.

I've done it in the past and I've gone to my swimming and I've come out thinking I survived that one, I didn't fall down the stairs and break my neck or I didn't fall into the swimming pool or I managed to find my locker – thank God there was somebody there to ask. You come out and you are more focused on 'I survived it' than 'well I feel better for doing that'. It's got to be user-friendly.
Female, 42, partially sighted, who
has progressively lost sight since age 16

Sometimes the lack of motivation was described as stemming from lack of will or 'apathy' in combination with the extra effort, rather like a cost-benefit analysis:

I'm admitting that I'm lazy regarding going round to the shop and having a walk. But I think what I can truly say about that is that the amount of effort required for me to do it isn't justified by the pleasure that I get.
Female, 56, hearing impairment in recent years

The effect of taking part in activity which is difficult can undermine disabled people's confidence, underlining physical inability rather than beneficial effects:

Although I think I'm quite a confident, outgoing person, I can feel useless enough without adding to it. So when a situation like that makes you feel useless, you avoid it.

Female, 42, partially sighted, who has progressively lost sight since age 16

There was a wide range of attitudes towards dealing with impairment barriers, though, on the whole, respondents expressed determination to overcome obstacles. This determination was motivated by a desire to retain independence:

It's taken me another week to get over it and go back and do it again, but I've gone back and done it again because I know damn well if you don't use it, you lose it. I don't want to be like that.

Female, 40s, partially sighted from birth

Some respondents' determination seemed to stem from a strong desire to distinguish themselves from other people who they felt had lost their determination. Not 'giving in' or not being 'couch potatoes' were important images for respondents.

I don't want to give in. I've seen that many patients give in ... I don't want to end up like that. I didn't want to give up exercise but there comes a point when you can't stand the pain.

Female, 33, physical disability since accident

To me if you're sitting back lulling in a chair all day, that to me is no good to you at all. There's times when I won't go up on the chair [stair lift], I will pull myself up on the chair rail.

Female, 68, physical and visual impairment since accident

These attitudes appeared to reflect an increased motivation among some respondents that had been developed in response to an impairment or to other people's expectations of inactivity. For example, one hearing impaired respondent had been effectively excluded from PE lessons at school because he was given extra English classes; he had felt this was because of an assumption on the part of the teachers that he would not be interested in sport. As a result, he had become involved in sport as an adult. Another respondent had encountered negative reactions from professionals and from her partner with regard to her doing any physical activity which had the effect of making her all the more determined:

The attitude was ... 'There's not much point in you doing anything, so long as you do a little bit of walking and keep walking, that's fine'. [For three years, she did no exercise, but then] I thought damn you, I will do things.

Female, 30s, multiple sclerosis, active

Seeing family or friends decline, or give in, and not wanting to do the same, was a further factor that was influential in terms of personal determination:

I watched my Dad die and he never, ever went in a wheelchair... he was determined. ... I want to be determined, I don't want to give in ... I'm only 34, I want to go on.
Female, 34, physical disability since accident

Levels of confidence

The potential to be put off physical activity because of the extra effort required heightened where someone lacked support or had low confidence or poor self-esteem.

At first you feel quite embarrassed about things and if you're quite withdrawn then it doesn't help. I'm quite lucky that I've got [her partner] who's very helpful and I've got quite a good family. Whereas if you were all on your own, if you lack confidence, you would just give in.
Female, 34, paralysis following car accident, active, wheelchair user

Sometimes some people have to be pushed. Some people will sit at home and do nothing; they feel like there's a barrier and people are going to look at them or laugh at them.
Male, 32, visual impairment

Lack of confidence sometimes had a direct impact on doing physical activity or on the choice of locations for doing it, for example, avoiding places where there would be strangers. It also had an indirect effect in terms of restricting mobility, because of anxiety about going out generally.

Among many respondents, there was a sense of self-consciousness about their impairment which, when acute, had a major effect on their ability to do things. The embarrassment was exacerbated for some by self-consciousness about being overweight.

It can build up in your mind that everybody's looking and thinking oh she's useless. But there is that embarrassment factor because you think everybody's doing this or whatever they are supposed to be doing and you're standing there trying to work out what they're doing and you just feel silly. The next time you think oh I don't want to go, I don't want to feel like that again and it does stop you.
Female, 42, partially sighted, who has progressively lost sight since age 16

I feel ashamed that I'm blind ... I feel that everyone is looking at me, feeling sorry for me, laughing at me.
Male, 50, blind in recent years, active

One of the reasons for feeling self-conscious was a strong sense of feeling different, or embarrassed that people won't realise that you are disabled if the impairment is not very visible:

People still look ... they're looking as if to see what the bloomin hell's wrong with her ... But it may be me that's looking round for people looking at me ... I feel safer here [at home] because nobody is watching me.
Female, 33, physical disability since accident

I feel abnormal. I'm not like anybody else. I feel excluded from everything. I feel different from everybody.
Female, 33, hearing impairment

Some respondents feel that they couldn't just turn up to a class or gym, because they would not know how they would '*fit in*', and would be embarrassed to ask for '*too much*' help.

Low confidence and feelings of isolation among deaf people can be caused by the particular difficulty of communication. Deaf respondents talked about becoming confident from doing activities with other deaf people, for example, playing in all-deaf teams.

Security fears added to low self-confidence for some, where there was fear of going out on their own, either at all, or in the dark, or due (as in one instance mentioned) to a threatening neighbour. Depending on the extent of support from family and friends, these feelings were also connected to depression, resulting in further withdrawal.

Where there was less self-consciousness, or where it had less effect on respondents' confidence to do things, it was sometimes the case that respondents had a determination to *overcome* embarrassment. There was a belief that confidence could be built by repeating an activity several times:

> *Every time you do that, it gets easier and easier.*
>
> Female, 56, hearing impairment in recent years

> *I don't care any more. If people don't like it, it's tough.*
>
> Male, 24, spina bifida, active, wheelchair user

> *I used to hate people staring, now I try to ignore it ... you have to get your confidence up.*
>
> Female, 34, paralysis following car accident, active, wheelchair user

However, for others there was a strong feeling that embarrassment was something that would never go away:

> *If I go into a public place ... somebody's always looking and that is my fear more than anything. It's what people are saying. I've had this a long time now, nine years, but it's still there and you still feel it, you never get over it, never.*
>
> Female, 33, wheelchair user

Variation at different times of life

Self-confidence and self-motivation varied at critical life stages. Retirement from work, for example, could result in further withdrawal and less activity. The effect of marriage breakdown or the death of a spouse also had a major effect on self-motivation to do physical activity. These changes in motivation at different times of life have also been demonstrated in other studies among the general population.

For respondents not disabled from birth, the onset of impairment in itself had a major effect on levels of self-confidence and attitude to activity.

> *I used to be terrible. For about the first two years I was not bothered about going out of the house full stop, I just wasn't fussed about it and I was going to stay in here forever.*
>
> Female, 34, paralysis since car accident, active, wheelchair user

If you've been injured, you have this grief period and then you come out of that and you've got rid of the anger and that, and you want to get on with life, but quite often in that period people are putting on weight, they're not looking after themselves. 'Health – it's not important any more, what can be worse than losing the use of my legs'. Female, 30s, multiple sclerosis, active

The onset of impairment, either sudden (through an accident or injury) or gradual, was perceived as being a critical factor in the change in the amount of physical activity done.

I used to run, I used to run marathons and I can't even run a mile, I can't walk a mile never mind run it.

Female, 33, back injury causing restricted mobility and severe pain

My sight had decreased – because I lost quite a bit of sight at one point. I think then I lost my confidence to do it, because I lost my confidence in the pool that I could just swim up and down my little lane and not get in any body else's way. Female, 42, visual impairment since age 16

However, onset of impairment was not the only factor in changes in amount of activity done. Other critical life stages included 'slowing down' as a result of ageing, which either happened at the same time as the onset of impairment, or had a separate effect, both before and after impairment.

For respondents where the onset of impairment was sudden, there was a recovery period, which sometimes included formal rehabilitation. The role of rehabilitation in becoming involved in physical activity can be critical. On the whole respondents' experiences of rehabilitation did not seem to have had a positive effect on taking up physical activity or sport.

Respondents, generally, talked about doing higher levels of physical activity in the past, particularly at school, and when they were younger. Leaving school or college and retiring from work were important stages, and having to spend a period of time in hospital sometimes meant losing a degree of fitness which was then difficult to regain.

Because I spent so much time in hospital I wasn't doing much and by the time I came out I had asthma and my chest and my back were too weak to take the strain of me doing all the sport I used to do ... I was devastated, I used to love doing my sport. My sport was part of my life for seven or eight years, I used to do it three times a week at school, every couple of weekends we used to go away, so it was a part of my everyday life really and then I just suddenly couldn't do it, it was quite devastating.

Female, 22, no use of legs, wheelchair user

Well since I left work, I think that's what kept me going because I thought when I was at work I never felt my aches and pains, couldn't of done, because I very seldom saw a doctor.

Female, 68, restricted leg mobility and pain, visual impairment

When you're younger I think you do a lot more anyway. You're out all the time, you're at work everyday and as you get older your body tells you that you can't do so much. Although you try to carry on. I often think, well I don't feel my age, so why can't I do this. You don't accept at first that you just can't do it anymore.   Male, 37, deaf from birth, active

3.3   Influence of others in affecting motivation

Given the low self-motivation felt among some respondents, there was a belief that disabled people sometimes needed more encouragement than the general population to take up physical activity. The influence of other people, both positive and negative, may therefore be particularly significant for this group.

Effect of school experiences

As in other studies, school seemed to have played both a positive and a negative role in respondents' attitudes to, and involvement in, physical activity. Several respondents spoke of bad experiences of physical activity at school, partly because of a dislike of the compulsion, or the competitive and team elements, of traditional school sports; others however, had felt encouraged and supported during their school years.

These differing experiences spanned both mainstream and special education. Some respondents who had been at *mainstream schools*, recalled negative experiences of being singled out or humiliated during sport, because of their impairment and sporting inability. A hearing impaired respondent had been excluded from school sport because his learning support classes took place during sports periods – a fact about which he felt very resentful. Instances were also mentioned of pupils with learning difficulties who had been barred from PE classes and were told to do homework in the library instead.

For respondents who had been to a special school, there were also mixed experiences, including some very positive memories of a wide range of varied activity – horse-riding, ice-skating, skiing and other less traditional sports. And:

It boosted your confidence ... at school we weren't taught that we were different.   Female, 45, blind from birth, active

Negative experiences of competitiveness and compulsion at special schools were also mentioned:

School always impressed on me that if I couldn't keep up with everybody else that I was basically no good ... It didn't help my attitude to fitness because of feeling that everything I did was not good enough in anybody else's eyes ... what was the point of bothering.   Male, 27, blind from birth

You went to another room to get out of the way so as he couldn't find you ..., but they would come and hunt you down ... Because that's what these schools are ... 'you come here so we rule you'.
     Male, 27, visual impairment, wheelchair user

In relation to students with learning difficulties, some special schools were said to lack a PE specialist equivalent to a PE teacher at a mainstream school. Experiences of sport or recreation at a special school could, therefore, be of poor quality, with provision inappropriate to pupils with the lowest level of ability. The emphasis of teacher training for special education was said to be more about caring; sport featured less.

Again, as with the non-disabled population, the transition from school was a critical point in either continuing or getting out of the habit of doing sport. Where involvement in sport at school had entailed special activities, respondents had difficulty continuing with the sport, as it often involved a great deal of travel to reach scattered facilities (see section 4.3).

Some respondents expressed views about the role of special schools in creating an environment where disabled people are sheltered from the real world, albeit in a supportive tight-knit community. Shifting from this environment to taking part in physical activity outside school was sometimes experienced as a shock.

I was in a special school for spastics, and I came out from an environment where I was one of the fittest into the outside world where I suddenly realised how great my disability was. Male, 49, cerebral palsy, active

I see this group from a deaf educated background who are very, very positive about their identity, but they're not responsible, they are not independent, mostly because it's been special schools, special teachers for them and they give them a lot of false hope, false impressions. And looking at this other group who've been mainstreamed, their development, they have a very positive sense of responsibility and independence and they learn about society and how it functions. Male, 46, profoundly deaf

At the same time, other respondents expressed some reservations about mainstream schooling, and felt there was a need to ensure an adequate level of support and provision for disabled children.

Influence of family and friends

On the whole, family and friends were a positive influence on respondents' motivation and, in some cases, a key factor in getting individuals started or continuing in physical activity. Some family members, or partners in particular, had been very encouraging, whereas friends were important both as motivators and as company. Wanting to do things, or to keep up with young children was also a key motivating factor for some respondents.

'I'm disabled so I can't do it' – they don't try, half of them. I used to feel like that. Our [daughter] won't let me, I think it's because I've got younger kids and they don't let you.
Female, 50, limited mobility due to brittle bones and severe asthma

My sister always taught me to be independent and strong, and to do whatever that I could do – emotionally, mentally and physically. So she's helped me a lot, she's encouraged me a lot to do things.
Female, 22, leg and back problems, wheelchair user

My boyfriend gets me doing all sorts ... I've thought of doing a lot more stuff since I've been with him than I would have done before.

Female, 22, leg and back problems, wheelchair user

I've got a good crowd of friends, more or less the same age, so we encourage each other. Male, 37, hearing impairment, active

Maybe getting a partner who's interested, that gets you going ... For me, it would have to be another person. Female, 53, hearing impairment, active

Similarly, the effect of lacking friends with whom to take part in physical activity, or friends being no longer available, was generally negative and discouraging. For some respondents, this was perceived as one of the main barriers. Some respondents had given up doing physical activity when their companion had stopped. This was particularly the case for respondents who wanted to do physical activity for the fun of it or for the social aspects, but was also a major factor for those who were, or felt, unable to do activities, or to get to activities, on their own.

I would love to do loads of things, but I've got no-one to go with.

Female, late-40s, partially-sighted

I don't go on my own ... Nobody to go with.

Female, 47, learning difficulties

Nobody to pick me up ... no, my mum won't let me go out walking.

Male, 33, learning difficulties

The significant influence of other people in relation to participation in physical activity applied across the impairment groups. It was an essential need for almost all the respondents with learning difficulties, and was particularly important among respondents with visual impairments, partly in a wish for company and partly a wish for someone to act as an 'introduction' or an initial pair of eyes. The difficulty of turning up alone and unannounced at a gym or class presented a significant barrier. This applied, too, to deaf respondents who often expressed the wish to have someone to do an activity with, particularly in terms of seeking other deaf people.

Having had one-to-one tuition in a particular activity had been a good way for some visually impaired respondents to get involved:

It was certainly easier to feel more confident in what I was doing when sometimes I was being physically shown what to do by somebody on a one-to-one. Male, 27, blind from birth

Although not a friend or family member in the strict sense, the significance of owning a dog provided a similar motivating factor for some respondents. This has also been demonstrated in other studies.

When you are alone and in the house you do have stages where you just don't want to go out and you are quite happy to just stay in the house. The dog really has made me better, by having the dog I've got to go out whether I want to or not. So therefore I have more exercise, because I've got the dog. Female, 53, hearing impairment, back pain, depression, active

Influence of disability sports groups

Disability sport, in the widest sense, was an important motivating factor for respondents who had become involved in regular physical activity.

This seemed to be particularly strong among the deaf respondents who were BSL users. The benefits of doing sport with only other deaf people was very important to these respondents, and getting involved in deaf sports after leaving school was a critical factor in whether sport was kept up or not.

In a similar way, respondents who were involved in a disability sports association (visited as part of this study) had very positive feelings about the role of the club in motivating individuals. Part of this seemed to revolve around adopting a sense of identity as 'disabled', viewed by members as a very positive thing, opening up opportunities to share information, as well as take part in activities, and part of it was connected to having the facilities and appropriate equipment available.

Then if you go to the club you see other people. When I first came I was thinking God almighty I don't know why they're smiling so much, why aren't they more miserable about life, they are stuck in a wheelchair. But when you get to go there a couple of times and they are all 'stop whittling on about that and just try and do' you stop yourselves from being so negative about everything.

Female, 34, paralysis since car accident, active, wheelchair user

I started enjoying sport more when I got to know a lot of my sort of people, visually impaired and blind people ... and saw how they were. More or less they had a normal life, they were doing all activities and stuff ... I trust and respect them.

Male, 32, visual impairment, deteriorating sight

If you're doing sport you meet people, you discuss what you're doing .. a lot of information comes from disabled groups when they're mixing, they share ideas and so on. Male, 56, physical disability since accident, active

Another advantage appeared to be the opportunity for disabled members to have contact with disability sports specialists and disabled achievers who could be key motivating individuals:

I said, 'Here we don't accept can't, we will try', and he made a special gadget so he could pull the bow, and it revolutionised his life.

Female, 60, about active, physically disabled husband

However, there were other respondents who either were not aware of disability sports, or would not be interested in that sort of opportunity (see section 5.1). One respondent had joined a disability swimming club on leaving school, but had not enjoyed the competitive nature of the activity:

I wanted to do it for the fun of it, and I found the group hard going really. It was very competitive and I wasn't into that ... the people who organised it were quite competitive, and there was quite a lot of pressure to compete.

Male, 31, cerebral palsy, wheelchair user

Influence of medical and other professionals

The medical profession and, in particular, GPs, had played a major role in influencing attitudes towards physical activity. Some respondents had been advised against doing a particular type of exercise, or against strenuous exercise in general where, for example, it might bring on epilepsy or if a respondent had suffered a heart attack. This advice was perceived as restrictive by some and as supportive by others.

He (GP) just says don't rush anywhere, just take your time and don't rush about.   Male, 52, hearing impairment, angina, asthma

The GP says, you must realise you can't do what you used to and to slow down, and take life a bit easier.
                              Female, 53, hearing impairment, back pain, depression, active

The doctor says, you shouldn't have done that … and it's just everyday ordinary things... that also makes you depressed.
                                         Female, 34, physical disability since accident

[Physiotherapists often say] if you live and work that is counted as exercise, because once you've done if you did more exercise you'd be too tired to live day to day, so it's an equation. Male, 49, cerebral palsy, active

Other respondents had received specific advice from their GPs or physiotherapists about the amount of physical activity they should be doing in relation to specific health or fitness objectives, or in relation to particular types of activity, for example swimming being a good form of physical activity. This was not always found helpful. Some respondents had received physiotherapy as part of a physical activity programme and, in some cases, this had been stopped as it was felt that it was too dangerous. One woman had been advised to take regular physical activity (similar to HEA guidelines) in order to control her weight level and high blood pressure. However, this advice had not been felt to be helpful because the GP was unable to suggest any activities that the respondent felt were suitable or realistic. She had found the experience very depressing.

Some respondents had received no personal advice at all, and were at a loss to know what to do:

Well you see activity can make your blood pressure higher and you can become hotter and much easier to sweat because of the high blood pressure and things like that. I asked the doctor, 'Can I do anything, can I do sports?' and he said 'Oh you can do anything you want' but I didn't feel that there was any advice, he just said, 'Oh you can do anything'.
                                                                 Male, 46, profoundly deaf

Nobody has ever offered me [advice about appropriate physical activity], nobody has ever suggested … [Although] I would like to do more, definitely, yes, … I don't want to sit in a chair and waste away.
                    Female, 64, limited by severe pain if standing/walking, by palpitations
                                           if moving rapidly, and by being very overweight

Hospitals and physiotherapists were criticised for their attitude towards exercise and physical activity during rehabilitation. For one respondent there was an insufficient emphasis on, or information about, 'sport'.

In hospitals they don't mention sport at all. I was doing basic physio, what they call sport there, and there's no information about sports.

Male, 56, physical disability since accident, active

The feeling was also expressed that rehabilitation [in the medical profession] made a distinction between impairment caused by accident and that caused by the onset of a neurological condition or old age:

Anybody who's not … 'we can make great bounds in their health and their mobility', they suddenly go, 'Lord I don't know what to do with them'.

Female, 30s, multiple sclerosis, active

Other influences

Although not asked specifically, there was virtually no mention of existing role models influencing disabled people to take up physical activity. This contrasts with the findings of earlier studies among the non-disabled population.

4 *Opportunity*

This chapter looks at the influences on participation in physical activity that might be said to be more external or extrinsic. It completes the picture of 'barriers' having examined ways by which impairment itself can restrict physical activities (Chapter 1) and having discussed motivational factors (Chapter 3). Since the right opportunity can serve as an incentive rather than a barrier, it also, by implication, shows suggestions for ways to encourage participation among disabled people.

While some of the issues described in this chapter apply also to non-disabled people, many others are more specific to those with disabilities. The data shows that in many ways external barriers can obstruct opportunities for disabled people to take part in physical activity or sport. The exact ways that they do so relates to the type and extent of impairment (among other factors) yet, in broad terms, are likely to centre around issues of access, taking this to include attitudes of providers and others. Access barriers featured far more in this study than in the earlier studies which documented attitudes and experiences among other groups of people. Of course, it was also acknowledged that physical activity could be done at home, but many disabled people, in common with others who are not disabled, placed a value on the social opportunities that physical activity afforded and the chance to 'get out'.

All the extrinsic factors that emerged across the interviews and discussions are summarised in Figure 4. It should be noted that the order of the points in Figure 4 does not indicate order of emphasis.

4.1   Awareness and information

A lack of awareness of the sort of activities that were physically safe and possible to do, on an individual level, has already been discussed in Chapter 1. This related to the specific nature of the impairment or disabling condition and lack of knowledge about what was suitable, or possibly, because of insufficient information in this respect.

Not knowing what physical activity they could, or would like to do, was a major factor for some respondents. While some seemed to have very little idea of what sorts of physical activity were available, others had tried many different types of activity, but felt they could not find anything suitable (either for their impairment or their preference).

I don't think there's any exercise I can do really when I've got this [ear condition].
                                   Male, 69, hearing impairment, balance problems

There's all these sports that I don't know about that blind people do and there must be some way or somewhere I can find out what's available.
                                   Male, 53, visual impairment, deteriorating sight

There isn't anything on the market you can actually buy for a disabled person to exercise ... we've tried all sorts.

Female, 33, spinal injury causing restricted mobility and severe pain

This was sometimes seen as the fault of people who might be expected to provide information about health and physical activity, for example, GPs:

Unless you went to hospital you wouldn't know nothing. Nobody comes round and tells you anything. They don't at your own doctors ... [tell you exercises] to help you breathe and how to move it off your chest, I didn't know none of that you see. And they should tell you when you first go on steroids really what it does entail.

Female, 50, brittle bones and severe asthma

One respondent, who was a member of a disability sports club, commented:

A lot of them would say that they don't know, they think, 'Well I'm disabled I can't do anything' and they need to be told what you can do.

Male, 24, spina bifida, active, wheelchair user

In addition, there appeared to be a general lack of awareness about what facilities or opportunities were available for doing physical activity. For example, some respondents knew what activity they wanted to do, but did not know of anywhere in their neighbourhood where they could go to do it.

There are disabled sports clubs about but you don't usually get to hear about them. There should be some way of letting people know about the facilities in different areas ... If you ask, people don't know so you have to find your information from other disabled people.

Male, 42, restricted use of legs since accident, wheelchair user

I think that often they do exist if only I knew where they were [classes for music and movement].

Male, 27, blind from birth

I have enquired ... [at] numerous places, but maybe it's the wrong places ... I don't know of any that do anything for disabled people.

Female, 33, spinal injury causing restricted mobility and severe pain

It was particularly important to know in advance whether or not facilities would be accessible and welcoming in relation to the disability. The fear that they might not be was a discouraging factor for some respondents.

You never know in advance how much they know about your disability ... Unless you know that you can leave the [guide dog] with somebody [while at the gym] it's just another worry really and it is another worry anyway if you leave them because you think, 'Are they behaving?' 'Are they settling?'

Female, 45, blind

People are frightened to go in case they haven't got the facilities or the help that they need.

Male, 33, visual impairment

If I went and it wasn't accessible it would put me off.

Male, 31, cerebral palsy, wheelchair user

Figure 4: Lack of opportunity regarding physical activity: external barriers to participation

> ***The range of issues mentioned:***
>
> **Finding out: awareness/information**
> - Information on an individual basis about safe suitable exercise re. the condition/impairment
>
> - Lack of information on specific suitable facilities or opportunities
>
> - Difficulties of access to information, including format of information, e.g. if blind or deaf
> Poor promotion to disabled people
>
> **Getting there**
> - Finding someone to go with
>   - for social reasons / enjoyment
>   - for assistance/as an interpreter/for moral support
>
> - Physical access to and from facilities
> e.g. transport mobility, disabled parking spaces
>   potentially long distances (due to lack of local provision)
>   security fears, e.g. going out alone/after dark
>
> **Provision (as experienced, or, as anticipated)**
> - Extent of suitable provision/facilities
>   - to participate in particular sport
>   - to participate with other disabled people
> - Cuts in provision
> - Poor access at facilities
>   - Physical aids/adaptations, for getting around and for use of equipment
>   - Need for extra assistance or special provision
>   - Restricted times of access
> - Attitudes
>   - of providers
>   (e.g. in relation to buildings design, and policies regarding disabled people)
>   - of staff
>   e.g. in relation to awareness of disabled issues, extent of welcome, helpfulness, fear or expectation of difficulties)
>   - of other users/participants
>   (possible negative attitudes)
>
> **Time and money**
> - Time
>   - Lack of time/other priorities
>   - Factors due to impairment in some cases:
>   (e.g. need to synchronise with helper's time/longer travel time to reach accessible facilities/reduced energy levels/activity can take longer)
> - Money
>   - Possible extra cost
>   - of transport (e.g. if need of taxis) to reach provision
>   - specialist equipment, e.g. sports wheelchair
>   - carer/assistance
>   - Other financial priorities

Along with the perception of a general lack of information about facilities, there was, not surprisingly, a sense that active promotion of such information was poor. Respondents' main sources of information seemed to be through informal networks, such as friends, family and disability groups, as well as through local newspapers or leaflets. Local authorities were criticised for being poor providers of information. Yet a local library or town hall was imagined by some respondents to be a first port of call if they were to set about seeking local opportunities. There was a general sense that disabled people had to go out and find their own information and that there were problems in doing this.

The format of information about opportunities to do physical activity was a further factor which made access to it problematic for some disabled people. Difficulties with printed information, for example, were not only described by respondents who had visual impairment but also by deaf respondents for whom BSL was their main language and who, therefore, were not fluent in English. With less access to oral information, some deaf people were doubly disadvantaged. The option to just go into a sports venue and ask for information was perceived to be not acceptable.

I'm frightened, I get concerned if I don't understand and there's no way for me to ask for clarification.   Female, 38, profoundly deaf

There were particular times of life when a lack of awareness of facilities for physical activity was said to present more of a barrier than at other times. Leaving school or college was mentioned as having left some respondents without the opportunities that they had become used to, and unaware of where to go to resume a particular activity. Other studies have shown that this is in common with non-disabled people.

I've no idea how to get started back up [since college], finding somewhere to go.   Female, 22, leg and back problems, wheelchair user

4.2   Someone to go with

Needing to find '*someone to go with*' as a spur to take part in physical activities was a theme across other studies with the non-disabled population and has been discussed in relation to disabled people in Chapter 3. For disabled people, this need carried further emphasis, for a variety of reasons. Some respondents stressed the social benefits of physical activity, both for general enjoyment, or specifically to alleviate isolation. The chance to get together with others who shared the disability was important, for example for some deaf people in order to communicate fully ('*Company to chat to ... others are not a part of my world – it's all about language*'). Some deaf respondents felt that opportunities to play sports with other deaf players were very limited, partly because it was difficult to find other deaf people in the local area.

There was also sometimes a need to be accompanied for moral support, or for physical assistance, including a need for an interpreter or 'a pair of eyes', and, for people with learning difficulties, for support and supervision. The lack of 'someone to go with' could present a barrier to participation.

No one to go with because I won't go swimming on my own.   Female, 30, learning difficulties

4.3   Getting there

A key enabling or disabling factor in respondents' ability to take part in physical activity was said to be access to facilities. This included both access at venues (see section 4.4) and also travel to and from a venue.

Transport mobility

Respondents in this study varied in the extent that they could travel and be mobile. Some had their own car and could drive to venues, although this might mean covering considerable distances to take part in their preferred activity and a need for sufficient disabled parking spaces in close proximity. Others could not drive, for a range of reasons, and were reliant on lifts, taxis, Dial-a-Ride or public transport, unless a venue was within walking distance (or pushing distance for those in wheelchairs). Even somewhere within walking distance was unsuitable for those who had difficulties walking or pushing, or where the disability (e.g. lack of sight) led to a reluctance to go out alone. Difficulties with inaccessible pedestrian environments were also described.

Some respondents spoke of the problems they had experienced in using different forms of transport. The use of buses, for example, was sometimes experienced as an embarrassment, especially by people who felt their movements were slow. The regular use of taxis was curtailed by their cost (although one respondent acknowledged the important role of disability benefits in helping towards this). Dial-a-Ride, seen as a useful alternative to taxis, presented a problem in needing to be booked a long time in advance of the planned journey. Guide dogs, an important aid to getting about, could only be used on routine journeys, and there were mixed views among owners about whether dogs should be left at an exercise venue.

Security

Some respondents had a fear about going out, especially alone. This appeared to be caused by a number of factors and was seen across the different impairment types, and across ages and gender. It had an impact partly in terms of getting to venues, but also on taking part in general outdoor activities, including walking. Some visually impaired respondents, in particular, would not go out on their own. For people with learning difficulties, the need to be accompanied was often a prerequisite, if not always by them, then by their carers:

Nobody to pick me up ... no, my mum won't let me go out walking.

Male, 34, learning difficulties

4.4   Provision

Provision is discussed here in terms of supply, physical access and, importantly, attitudes among providers towards disabled people. It relates mainly to accessible sports/leisure facilities, including organised sport.

*If you're talking like just with pushing your chair and that, then no,
it's not really any different [doing physical exercise] because you can
always do that when you've got your chair. But if you're talking like
sportswise, actually going out and doing sport, then yes it's a lot more
difficult because it's a case of having to find places that are accessible
… So in that way it is a lot harder.*

Female, 34, paralysis since car accident, active, wheelchair user

Locally based provision

The extent of suitable provision for accessible sports or activities was said to be limited. This might relate to a particular sport or activity that was preferred or to the wish to do it with a particular group of people, for example those who shared the disability. Cuts in provision were noted, as in the amount of organised deaf sport, or (for people with learning difficulties) in swimming sessions from day centres.

*I don't go now [swimming] because they cancelled it. They cancelled the
swimming. Now I don't go.*   Female, 47, learning difficulties

*There's nothing round here to do … Sometimes I get bored with being
indoors and I like to get out.*   Female, 27, mild learning difficulties,
enjoys physical activity, quite active, concerned about health

There was likely to be a need, therefore, to search out opportunities to take part in an organised sport or for accessible facilities, and perhaps to travel long distances to reach them because of the limited supply. One respondent, for example, had searched for many years before he found a venue where he could practice a particular sport (wheelchair archery) and then travelled some thirty miles on a regular basis to reach it.

Accessible facilities

A major barrier, therefore, was lack of accessible facilities that were within easy travelling distance, given restricted transport mobility. In some cases, this related to respondents' lack of awareness of information about such facilities, whereas others knew that there was nothing available.

Accessibility at venues meant different things to different respondents, in part depending on the nature of their impairment. Access at a basic level, for some respondents, meant being able to get inside the venue and being able to use any equipment provided. Problems in access were described in this study in relation to:

- insufficient parking spaces: a lack of disabled spaces and the fact that their use was not enforced. (One respondent felt that there should be at least 10 or 15 spaces at any venue so that disabled people did not need to worry beforehand about whether or not they would be able to park.)

- steps/stairs preventing wheelchair access

- hoist into/out of the pool

- size of changing cubicles or toilets (for wheelchair users)

- steps marked in colour contrast for guidance of visually impaired

- non-adapted equipment or facilities, e.g. swimming pool too cold, or aerobic

- equipment not adapted for use by hand

- permission for guide dog

- alarm system inappropriate for deaf people (one deaf respondent had made special arrangements with the venue manager about being alerted if an emergency alarm sounded).

Provision of accessible facilities also covered level of staff available and the spaciousness or quietness of a venue. This was an important factor for some respondents with visual impairments and also for some respondents who were afraid of injury or accidents.

Some respondents made a distinction between elements of access that were essential and those that were preferred. For example, a swimming pool was usable for a wheelchair user even though the changing cubicles were very small and showers inaccessible. However, a hoist and help to get in and out of the pool was essential. In this case, the helpfulness of the staff was stressed, and appeared to be an additional factor in making somewhere useable, where access was less than ideal.

Provision of aids or equipment at an individual level was also important to some respondents. One local authority was criticised for being apparently reluctant to provide a special sports wheelchair. Another respondent had been refused a guide dog and felt that this was a major cause of his inactivity as he could not go out walking.

Attitudes of providers and others

An important aspect of accessible facilities encompassed the attitudes of providers and staff at sports/leisure facilities, for example, from the point of view of the welcome accorded and the extent of awareness that staff had of the needs of disabled people. This included attitudes which were manifested at policy level regarding the inclusion or exclusion of people with particular impairments, or the restriction, either directly or indirectly, on when they could take part. Although some respondents reported no problems in this regard or had positive encounters of being made to feel welcome, several experiences of attitudes as a barrier to participation were recounted across the study. There were instances, for example, of a general lack of understanding regarding the effects of the impairment disability:

I don't go swimming anymore because the local centre just doesn't understand ... you can get very physically fatigued, and my balance is a major problem I have at the moment ... Walking along a wet floor I'm so scared of falling down .... So if I'm crawling along the wall, then let me be, but often if you do that, they look at you as if to say well are you an alcoholic or are you drunk or something like that.

Female, 30s, multiple sclerosis

*[At the gym] young people there, say teenagers who come and teach you,
and they are confused about the deafness and I have to try and relax them
and they give me only brief information. It's them that's embarrassed and
we swap notes and things like that and I have to try and make them relax.
But I'm used to that, that happens in so many places that I go.*

Male, 46, profoundly deaf

and also of:

- refusal for membership

*I have been to the [private] gym and they've refused me because I'm too
much of a high risk on insurance.*

Female, 33, spinal injury causing restricted mobility and severe pain

- access to a swimming pool restricted solely to special disabled swimming
  sessions, unless accompanied by non-disabled helpers; a point about
  which this respondent was:

*Very angry ... because as far as I'm concerned I'm as able bodied as
anyone else in the water.*

Male, 42, restricted use of legs since accident, wheelchair user

- negative response to leaving a guide dog at a sports venue, with the
  expectation instead of being accompanied by a sighted friend.

The enormous importance of disability-educated and welcoming staff and
instructors was also made clear from respondents' suggestions for ways of making
physical activity more attractive (See Chapter 5).

Several respondents had no direct experience of the use of sports facilities as a
disabled person but, because of negative attitudes that they had encountered
elsewhere, the expectation of difficulties with sports providers or staff was, for
some, an important factor that could act as a barrier to participation.

*People try to pre-judge you ... You try to fit in ... You have to explain in
advance that you can't see. 'Can you join?' etc. They'd be frightened that
you'd have an accident or something.* Female, 45, blind from birth, active

*If I went to a canoe club, it's highly likely that they wouldn't have a clue
what to do with me. It would be difficult for them and difficult for me ...
that would make me reluctant to do it.*

Male, 31, cerebral palsy, wheelchair user

There was also a general feeling that attitudes of other facility-users towards
disability, and towards disabled people, might be negative. Illustrations were given
of negative experiences with the general public in a wide range of circumstances,
such as on public transport. Although there was recognition that negative attitudes
were often based on ignorance or uncertainty (e.g. '*If it's people's first encounter
with a disabled person they don't know how to react*') this, nevertheless, could
have a major discouraging effect on confidence and motivation to try out an
activity. It was influenced in turn by respondents' own attitude and levels of self-
confidence (discussed in Chapter 3), as well as by the nature of their impairment
or condition and the amount of help or assistance needed. Some felt more
comfortable than others about asking for help or explanations.

4.5   Time and money

Time

Lack of time as a barrier to physical activity was cited by respondents in two different situations: by people in employment or training, and by those with caring responsibilities. For some of these respondents it was perceived as the main barrier. Some with dependent children, for example, primarily women, found difficulties with fitting special sessions or exercise classes into their domestic routine or in finding the opportunity to do physical activity at particular times when they were free.

> *It's finding the time to do it, there isn't enough hours in the day.*
>
> Female, 33, hearing impairment, lone mother of three

This was found in the earlier studies and was echoed here. There was recognition, too, that time as a barrier to physical activity was also related to priorities rather than to absolute time.

> *I can make time for physical activity … I make time for all the other things I want to do, so it's the other issues really.*
>
> Female, 42, partially sighted, who has progressively lost sight since age 16

However, prioritising time in this way was also seen as particularly important for disabled people in order to avoid isolation that might arise from the impairment. Such priorities might be for socialising rather than for physical activity.

> *Socialising is more important [than physical activity] when you meet up… It means that our emotional needs are met, we are happier.*
>
> Female, 38, profoundly deaf

Or, the priorities might be to focus on just one particular activity known to be accessible or enjoyed.

> *I'm not going to distract myself away from archery; I can only think of one thing at a time otherwise I won't do it as well.*
>
> Male, 24, spina bifida, wheelchair user

Time can be more significant as a barrier to participation for disabled people than for the non-disabled, for a number of reasons:

- when lack of time is combined with reduced energy levels, **in the time that is available** for physical activity

- **longer travel time** when accessible facilities are further away

- the need to find and set aside a longer time slot when **activity takes longer** due to an impairment

- the need to **spend time finding someone** else to do the activity with and at mutually convenient times

- difficulties in **synchronising the timing of local authority transport provision with volunteer activity** for those who depend on it, such as those with learning difficulties.

Money

The financial cost of physical activity was mentioned, but did not seem to be a major deterrent factor to doing physical activity. Some respondents pointed out that the use of money was a question of choice,

[If I had more money] I would go out and exercise but it wouldn't be doing proper exercise, I would just go out dancing and enjoying myself.

Female, 20, visual impairment, who evidently did not count dancing as 'proper exercise'

and there was recognition that, for most people, exercise and physical activity did not need to be expensive:

I don't think money would actually stop me doing exercise, unless you were paying … like sports centres and things. Don't see sense in that as you can … do it [exercise] yourself.
Male, 69, hearing impairment

However, cost was clearly a key factor in the *choice* of activity. The cost of a private gym or health club membership, for example, ruled this out as an option for those not in full-time employment.

Well, it doesn't cost you nowt to go for a walk and things like that, and that's as good as any exercise there is, I think. If I wanted to go to the gym I couldn't afford it. I think what they are doing there I could do myself at home.
Male, 69, hearing impairment

I'd like to go to step aerobics, like a class, but I can't really afford it now, because I'm signing on.
Female, 27, learning difficulties

Financial considerations were also sometimes a secondary factor in influencing the *amount* of activity that was done.

I would like to but then it's so expensive because I'm on limited income now, I can't do it every day. Because they say they don't give discount for disabled people, we pay £3.05 for the lesson.
Female, 58, partially sighted and some restricted mobility since accident

With providers now more amenable to addressing financial barriers (as pointed out in the consultation interviews), it is perhaps not surprising that cost is said to be less of a problem than it once was. Yet some older disabled respondents did express the view that activities were too expensive and should be discounted further.

In comparison with the non-disabled population, taking part in physical activity can cost extra money. There were instances of this in the current study, for example, because of:

- **the cost of transport** – taxis may be needed, or longer (thus more expensive) journeys in general to reach accessible facilities

- **the cost of specialist equipment**, such as a sports wheelchair

- **the need to pay for assistance**, for example, paying entrance and travel for a sighted friend to accompany someone who is blind.

5 Suggestions for promotion and provision

This chapter presents respondents' views about what would make physical activity easier or encourage greater take-up. It is based primarily on respondents' own suggestions, many of which are implicit in the motivators and barriers described in Chapters 3 and 4.

Suggestions covered issues of provision, including preferred activity and preferred setting, access to facilities, changing the attitudes of providers, and promotion to increase awareness about physical activity and exercise options.

5.1 Preferences and choices

Type of exercise or activity

Preferences or aspirations in relation to types of physical activity were very mixed – there was no clear picture of any activity type or types that might be appropriate for disabled people as a whole, or for any of the specific impairment categories. This is probably to be expected, given the diversity of the sample and of the disabled population.

Exercise aspirations appeared to be fairly limited. Easy-access and the more every-day activities such as walking/pushing, swimming, cycling, gardening, gyms or health clubs, and exercise classes were the main activities that respondents across all impairment categories either already did, or wanted to do. Some respondents also wanted more specialist sports or adapted sports such as wheelchair athletics, basketball, archery, blind cricket or bowls, or horse-riding. There was also some interest in 'adventure' activities, like skiing, hang-gliding, and sailing.

There were, of course, personal likes and dislikes of particular activities. Swimming, for example, was favoured by many respondents, but others were frightened of water or could not swim. Gyms or exercise machines also had mixed reviews: for some respondents, for example, the lack of direct achievement in '*not getting anywhere*' on an exercise bike was felt to be very frustrating.

The image which some respondents had of certain activities or the image of their own skills in relation to activities also shaped their preferences.

I don't do them exercises that women's doing – singing and dancing … all that carry on.   Male, 69, hearing impairment since childhood

I'd be hopeless at a gym compared to people who go regularly.
Female, 45, blind from birth

There were mixed views about whether a 'sporty' activity was desirable or not. Some respondents felt that only 'proper' exercise counted, which meant that they excluded dancing, or '*just walking*' from the definition of physical activity.

However, others were put off by a sporty image, or '*pumping iron type*' activities and preferred less '*macho*' or more alternative exercise:

> *If I had the encouragement to do more in the way of dance ... then I might be persuaded.*
>   Male, 27, blind from birth

The type of activities provided especially for disabled people were sometimes regarded as unsuitable because they were seen as being aimed at older or more frail people. Keep fit or blind bowls at a blind centre were examples where younger visually impaired people felt that the provision did not cater for their needs.

Respondents whose impairment placed severe physical limitations on what they could do, perceived that their choices were very limited, although this was partly shaped by ignorance of what physical activity they could do (see Chapters 1 and 4):

> *There aren't a lot of ways to exercise, because you've only got your arms, so if they could come up with something then, yes, that would be helpful.*
>   Female, 34, paralysed from chest down, active

> *If somebody could invent something for those muscles that aren't being used.*   Female, 33, back injury causing severe pain and restricted mobility

Preferred setting or style of provision

Views about preferred setting or location for doing physical activity were also very mixed. The most contentious issue among respondents was whether they preferred activity solely with other disabled people, or as part of mainstream provision.

A number of respondents were, or had been, involved in deaf or disability sports, that is, sport that is organised separately by, and for, disabled people through disability organisations. Among these respondents, there was a strong preference for separate provision of activity. For deaf respondents (BSL users) this was mainly for reasons of ease of shared language and communication, particularly for team sports. For visually and physically impaired respondents, it provided an opportunity to take part in adapted activities or the use of special equipment, and was also about feeling at ease. This preference was in the context of being happy to play against, or compete with, non-disabled people. There were very positive feelings among this group of respondents about taking part in physical activity, sometimes combined with a strong desire to involve others:

> *You want to stay involved – the atmosphere, it's so brilliant, it's wonderful.*
>   Male, 56, restricted mobility, speech impairment since accident, active

> *There are people who won't come because it's a club for disabled and they don't want to be classed as 'disabled' ... They need to realise it's no disgrace and it's no shame.*   Female, 60, partially sighted, arthritis

This kind of provision was seen as a major motivating factor for some respondents:

> *It really needs to be more deaf groups, only for deaf, that would be wonderful. There are college courses for deaf people and deaf people gain confidence from that and sports. You need that.*
>   Female, 38, profoundly deaf since childhood

There was no perceived need for impairment-specific provision except among BSL users who felt strongly about team sports with deaf only participants, and among some older respondents who preferred the idea of activity solely with their own age group. For disabled people involved in competitive sport, competitions are sometimes organised into complex impairment-specific classification systems.

Outside of the experiences and views of respondents involved in sport specifically with other disabled people, there was also a strong view that some special provision had an important role to play. Special provision could mean a range of things, both within and separate to mainstream provision. The main features of special provision seemed to be as follows:

- having extra help, supervision or tuition
- classes conducted at a slower pace
- separate sessions avoiding crowds or busy times, and
- having an 'introduction' to a mainstream class or activity, which might include separate one-to-one tuition.

Where respondents wanted separate provision, this was very clearly linked to levels of confidence or self-consciousness:

Somewhere you could go and someone could explain what it entails, maybe just for tea or coffee, or introduce you to someone who runs a class, then you think, 'Oh I've met that person so I'll go because I know they're all right or I know so and so's going so maybe I'll go down'.

Female, 53, hearing impairment, lip reads

What I'd really like to do is go with someone first, see what I made of it, what the people were like and if I felt comfortable, I wouldn't mind then ... it's nice to feel that people won't patronise you.

Female, 45, blind from birth

If it existed I would go ... Maybe it would bring me out a bit more.

Female, 33, hearing impairment, lip reads

[With disabled only] It's not so embarrassing, you're all in the same boat.

Female, 68, restricted mobility, pain, visual impairment

A fear of injury, accident or overdoing it also led to a preference for special provision which involved supervision or separate sessions:

Somebody there to jump in at any time ... I always fear that my leg's going to stop and I'm going to go under ... If you go to some baths today, you can't get in without being kicked, punched, dived on.

Female, 33, back injury causing restricted mobility and severe pain

Separate provision was sometimes suggested for pragmatic reasons, in order to make use of existing organisations or facilities. For example, there was some suggestion that provision could be organised through day centres, either by setting up classes or by providing special gym facilities. Because of the way day centres are managed, activities would probably be impairment-specific, although this did not appear to be the intention behind the suggestion.

However, across all impairment groups, special provision was put in the context of an overall aim of integration. The rationale for this was described as firstly, wanting to be perceived as normal and not 'special', and secondly, to raise the general public's awareness of disability.

You shouldn't all be clubbed together. I don't mind being with other disabled, but sometimes you feel as if they all want you just shoved in a corner and leave you there ... You want a choice [of activity], especially if you're young and single. **Female, 34, paralysed from chest down, active**

The wish for special provision in the context of an aim of integration sometimes raised contradictions. One woman, who expressed a preference for separate sessions at a gym or aerobics class, also had a strong reaction against special provision which she perceived as patronising:

I don't want to join a group of disabled people, 'Come on all you nice little disabled people'... on balance I'd choose integration, because I'm no different from you. **Female, 42, visual impairment**

I can see advantages in both really. I think I would want both ... Although if I think about it now I tend to find that when things are directed at me as a blind person, I tend to find a lot of so called blind communities, it tends to bring on feelings of insularity and exclusivity and there are times when I find with myself that I wouldn't necessarily want to do things just with other blind people ... What I would not what to happen is to find that there are certain activities that are recommended for 'the blind' to do and targeted only at the blind without finding that that activity is recommended to everybody else as well. **Male, 27, blind from birth**

At the same time, one respondent commented:

I wouldn't want to be the only blind person in a situation, because then sighted people do their own things, and you get left out or excluded. **Male, 50, blind in recent years**

Some respondents had strong feelings against separate provision, especially where it was perceived to be the only option available. One of the factors that turned respondents against special provision was the feeling that it meant activities could not be shared with non-disabled family or friends:

They've got all these activities, it doesn't say nothing about your partner going along, which to me isn't fair. **Male, 33, visual impairment since childhood, active**

Just because you're disabled, why should you be any different to any other family? It does upset me for the lad ... I think we lose out on a lot ... It's not fair on him. **Male, 42, spinal injury, wheelchair user part-time**

Respondents' views about separate or mainstream activity appeared to be partly shaped by their preferences for how and where they enjoyed doing activity in a more general sense, for example, at home or on their own, compared with in a group or an organised session. Some were motivated by team sports and by competition, whereas others had a strong reaction against competition or saw advantages to activities which could be done at an individual level.

5.2   Access to venues and activities

Access to venues and activities is clearly a critical factor in disabled people's ability to take part in physical activity. Respondents did not make specific suggestions as to how physical access could be improved, although much can be implied from the access barriers described in Chapter 4.

In addition to physical access, some respondents also emphasised the importance of activities being cost-subsidised to encourage disabled people to use them. Transport access was also a significant issue for respondents (described in Chapter 4).

Specific suggestions from respondents for improving physical access included:

- the monitoring of disabled car-parking
- gym equipment well spaced
- access to equipment, including adapted equipment for wheelchair users/use by hand
- Braille indicators on equipment, talking machines, or pictorial (rather than text) instructions (for deaf users)
- colour contrast on equipment
- heated swimming pools.

The provision of more information, and the availability of information about access features of local facilities was suggested across all impairment categories. This was sometimes based on experience of not knowing where to go for information or finding existing information sources (such as local councils) unhelpful. Local newspapers, leaflets, disability schemes or organisations, and local shops or libraries were all suggested as vehicles for displaying printed information.

There was also a view that the promotion of facilities in general needs to make it clear that disabled people are welcome. This would help to go some way towards countering disabled people's fear of just turning up, uncertain about the reception they would receive.

Awareness training for providers

For some respondents, the degree to which facilities or venues was accessible was very much shaped by the role of staff. This could work in a number of ways, for example, help and assistance from staff could change a physically inaccessible facility to a usable one, or vice versa. For people with sensory impairments, lack of access is often about communication barriers, and the role of staff is again critical.

This led some respondents to see awareness training for staff as a key factor in encouraging them to take part in physical activity.

*It's about knowing how to approach people and not make them feel
any different, that's the secret ... Make people available to them that
understood their disability ... you can't just stand up in a class or go
to the tutor and say, 'How much do you know about so and so?'*

Female, 45, blind from birth

For deaf people who use BSL, the ability to communicate with staff is a major
factor:

*My dream is that everyone could sign and it would mean that I would be
able to relax and be natural and that's a real dream.*

Male, 23, profoundly deaf since childhood

Negative attitudes of staff were also seen by respondents as resulting in
exclusionary policies and restrictive provision, and awareness training was
suggested as a means of encouraging a more inclusive approach.

5.3   Information and promotional material

A key issue to emerge from the research is the need for more information to be
made available to disabled people about the benefits of physical activity and
exercise options. Health promotion, apart from through the medical profession,
was not something that respondents were aware of. There was some recognition
of the influence of television and magazines on general opinion forming, but this
did not play a very large part in respondents' attitudes. Some respondents
complained that representations of physical activity on television were always
young, fit, active females, rather than elderly or disabled people. The one exception
to this appeared to be *Mr Motivator* who had run a special set of programmes on
exercise for disabled people:

*It was really good, it had exercise for people sitting in a chair. Someone
had written in and they'd realised that not everyone can do it.*

Female, 22, severely restricted mobility from birth, wheelchair user

General strategies for promotion to providers and medical and other professionals,
as well as to disabled people, are suggested in the recommendations in Chapter 6.

What to promote to disabled people

Apart from a belief in the need for general awareness-raising about the benefits of
physical activity, respondents did not suggest any clear thoughts about the level or
types of physical activity that should be promoted. There was a general feeling that
promotion about prescriptions, for many disabled people, could only be done at
an individual level. An exception to this, however, was found among deaf
respondents for whom general awareness raising campaigns, in an appropriate
format, might be beneficial.

One of the key areas where respondents felt they did not have sufficient
information was on the type of physical activity options available. This could be
at a very individual level, or could be a more general promotion, in terms of the
range of activities that exist.

Some respondents suggested that disabled people needed extra encouragement or motivation. This might be done through the use of positive images and role models of disabled people in the media and in other promotional material.

I think possibly partnership might be a good idea, you know, showing disabled people and able bodied people doing things together ... If you can show disabled people at the beginning of a disability that they can end up participating against able-bodied people on an even basis, like you can in archery ... That is something they need to understand – that just because you're disabled doesn't mean to say you're put in a box, and say, 'You're disabled, you've got to do it this way, and you're able-bodied you've got to do it this way'.
Female, 60, visual impairment, arthritis

I think it's got to be clear that it's aimed at disabled people. If they don't do that, disabled people won't notice it.
Male, 31, spina bifida, wheelchair user

However, there was a feeling that this should not be about making 'Super-heroes', which would deter people, but that '*it's got to be directed at ordinary people*'.

Using disabled people to carry out promotion messages was also suggested by one respondent who had worked herself in health promotion to older people:

I use myself, I'm disabled ... I used to say 'Look I've lost the sight in one eye, that doesn't mean I have to stop living, that doesn't mean I can't do things.' So normally I use myself as an example.
Female, 58, visual impairment, stiffness in legs

How and where to promote to disabled people

It was suggested that information should be made available through a number of different avenues and in different formats. In addition, there was a feeling that for *some* disabled people, information and advice should be made available by the medical profession.

Using printed or other material

Awareness-raising campaigns aimed at disabled people were suggested as a way of overcoming the lack of knowledge about the benefits of physical activity. Some respondents suggested there could also be general awareness campaigns on television or radio or in national newspapers. However, it was also suggested that while the promotional message should be fairly general (not impairment specific), the use of different avenues of promotion for different impairment groups was a good idea.

The need to target different groups using a range of methods is partly because of the use of, and preference for, different media. For example, because written material can be a problem for deaf respondents who used BSL, it was suggested that promotion could be done through signers at deaf clubs, videos with BSL or sub-titles, and the use of teletext for any television material. Respondents with visual impairments suggested the use of tapes, talking newspapers and Braille for promotional material. National disability networks were suggested as a media for raising awareness and again, use of these would, on the whole, be targeted at specific impairment groups, for example, the RNIB or BDA clubs and newsletters. National disability newsletters, such as *Disability Now*, were also suggested.

Other respondents felt that written material was not the best format for information, and were more comfortable with spoken material, either on the national media or in person.

I'm not a person that can take things in very easy and I'm not a reader ...
I have to read it over a few times before it sinks in.

Female, 64, restricted mobility, arthritis, weight problem

There was also a feeling that information could be targeted at disabled people at a *local* level. Again, this included information both about physical activity in general as well as about facilities. Suggestions for where information could be best placed to reach disabled people included:

- local libraries and local shops, CABx

- disability groups and day centres

- local disability press, or schemes such as Shopmobility

- local papers or information through the letterbox

- leafleting of all registered disabled.

One of the difficulties of targeting disabled people, which was raised by disability organisations during the consultation stage of this study, is that many may not identify themselves as disabled; for example, older people with a visual or hearing impairment may just regard this as part of ageing. They may not therefore see promotional messages or images aimed at disabled people as applying to them. In addition, the greater integration of some disabled people into the community, such as those with learning difficulties, makes direct targeting of information far more difficult.

Through medical or other professionals

Some respondents held the view that doctors and the medical profession had an important role to play in the promotion of physical activity messages. It was felt that GPs, in particular, were in a strong position to advise people at an individual level about what they can and cannot do in relation to physical activity.

For one group of disabled people, who have hospital treatment as a result of the onset of disability, there was a view that hospitals and physiotherapists ought to be a better source of information than they currently are. Raising awareness at an individual level appeared to be something that was felt to be important:

I think that before you leave hospital they should promote the fact, they
actually sit down and tell you you've got to do more exercise ... explaining
the fact that you are not going to be burning up as much energy as a
normal person in moving about and this is why you've got to go and make
an effort. Then say where different clubs are within your area of the
country or something ... Then when you do go back for outpatients that
they should regularly talk about what physical activities you're doing,
regularly get you weighed and if you are putting on weight, find out why
you're putting on weight. Female, 34, paralysed from chest down, active

*If people are discharged from hospital they should be given a pack
showing their nearest sports club to encourage them to go along.*

Female, 60, visual impairment, arthritis

There were mixed views about the medical profession. There appeared to be a general belief that it was their role as medical experts to provide advice and reassurance about appropriate levels of physical activity and, for some respondents, having such advice was an important factor in feeling confident about doing physical activity. However, some respondents were sceptical about the extent to which the medical profession themselves have the necessary information or expertise to advise disabled people.

*Quite often the medical profession don't realise what you can do anyway.
They could be saying, 'You can be fit and healthy, you can eat properly'.*

Female, 30s, multiple sclerosis, active

Providing both general and specific advice and information *face-to-face* seemed to be important:

*For elderly groups I think if you go and explain it to them. Even younger
people I find, they take a leaflet and find half the time they don't read it
because they haven't got the time. They think I'll read it and somebody
who is a busy mother, got two or three kids, she doesn't allow the time
for herself.*

Female, 58, visual impairment, stiffness in legs,
used to work as health promoter

Other professionals, such as disability sports officers, were also mentioned as a potentially good source of promotional material and activities.

Partnership between different professionals was also suggested, for example across different local authority departments and including the voluntary sector. This was suggested especially in relation to people with learning difficulties, so that access to this group could be facilitated through links between day centres, social services and the voluntary sector.

While it was generally felt that promotion and more information would be positive, some respondents said that they would react badly if they felt that they were being specifically targeted for a message to 'disabled people' or if they felt they were being pressurised into doing activity:

*I do it out of my own choice, not because someone is telling me to do it.
I probably wouldn't do it if someone was telling me.*

Female, 20, visual impairment in recent years

In addition, one respondent cautioned the use of promotion without putting other measures in place such as improved accessible facilities:

*I think it's important to make sure the services are there, before they start
the promotion. Because there's no point in promoting exercise for disabled
people then finding out there's nowhere to go.*

Male, 31, cerebral palsy, wheelchair user

6 *Overview and recommendations*

This chapter highlights some key issues pertinent to the promotion of information about physical activity to disabled people. The evidence from the study points to a need to promote and relevant issues are outlined here.

6.1 A need to promote information about physical activity

Doubts and uncertainty about physical activity as a disabled person

The evidence from this study points to a clear need for disabled people to receive information regarding physical activity. This is based, in particular, on the findings that:

- Some disabled people have a low awareness of the beneficial effects of physical activity and have not come across health messages in this respect.

- Knowledge of existing guidelines about beneficial levels of physical activity and about the significance of the extent of physical activity in relation to health, was also found to be low.

- This low awareness and knowledge appears to contrast with that demonstrated in earlier studies in this series among non-disabled groups of the population.

- Where the promotion of physical activity guidelines had been encountered, there was uncertainty among some disabled people about whether or not these were applicable to them, given the type or extent of their disability.

Difficulties in taking part in physical activity as a disabled person

In terms of taking part in physical activity, this uncertainty or lack of information is exacerbated by further barriers:

- Although many barriers to taking part in physical activity apply to all groups of the population, there is clear evidence of additional barriers for disabled people. These can relate to the effect of the impairment and to the intrinsic and extrinsic barriers to physical activity, as documented throughout this report.

- The barriers often trace back to difficulties of access to physical activity, taking the term 'access' in its widest sense.

The need for promotion

It could be argued, therefore, that there is a need for *extra* encouragement for, and promotion of physical activity to, disabled people. Several of the disabled people interviewed expressed a wish for such information.

Yet the manner of any promotion needs to bear in mind two important points. When encouraging the take-up of physical activity among disabled people, there is a need also to promote:

- **Information on accessible facilities and activities**
  This is essential since so many barriers to take-up relate to levels of access and expectations of inaccessibility.

- **Individualised programmes**
  There can be a need for information and advice on an individual basis for some disabled people, related to the type and extent of their impairment. For example, physical activity programmes may need to be designed at an individual level.

6.2 Avenues for promotion

Concern about direct promotion to 'disabled people' in general

Despite the need for information on physical activity, direct promotion of information to 'disabled people' as a single group is often inappropriate. This is because of:

- The wide diversity of the population and their differing physical abilities.

- Difficulties in targeting some disabled people, in terms of how to find and make contact with them.

- Sensitivity to 'disabled' labels among some people, including those who would not necessarily identify themselves as 'disabled' nor be susceptible to direct promotion to 'disabled people'.

- The inappropriateness of blanket prescription of specified physical activity guidelines. Additionally, some groups of physically disabled people may not think messages are aimed at them if their perception is that they are unable to do any activity, or any vigorous activity.

Therefore, there would be a need for different promotional angles for different disability groups, and for other specific avenues of promotion.

Suggested avenues for indirect promotion

The research findings suggest that a many-sided approach to promotion strategies might be appropriate. This would involve action with different groups and **partnership** within and between these different groups.

These different groups might include:

- medical professionals (GPs, physiotherapists, hospitals, spinal injury units)

- local services (day centres, disability sports officers, care workers)

- disability groups – both general and sports groups; local and national networks, information and advice organisations

- schools, colleges (PE specialists and others).

The aim would be to promote awareness of:

- **The health benefits of physical activity.**

- **The add-on benefits**, such as social benefits, increased independence and confidence. For example, promotion of physical activity as an integral part of a care plan to include all aspects of daily life.

- **Individualised programmes of activity** (medical professionals in particular).

Since prescriptions to disabled people may need to be tailored to the individual, professionals can have an important role to play. The extent of their knowledge and their attitude towards what activities *can* be done has an important influence on some disabled people's involvement in physical activity.

However, the research is clear that professionals need to avoid being authoritarian or patronising in their approach to disabled people. Professionals also need to recognise the wish for a range of activity types and not push people into particular stereotype activities.

Information format and images

Consideration of the following points needs to be borne in mind in any promotion:

- format of information appropriate to the disability type
  e.g tape/video, textual/verbal/pictorial/Braille/BSL

- including positive images of disabled people, and ordinary people, not super-heroes

- consideration of role models? There was a notable absence of named role models across this study.

6.3 Work with providers

Given that lack of access at sport and leisure facilities and negative attitudes of other people have emerged in this study as a major barrier for disabled people, promotional work, either directly or indirectly, to disabled people is only part of the picture.

Promotional work with providers of sports and leisure facilities, perhaps in partnership with local disabled people, might include encouraging:

- the provision of accessible, local and welcoming facilities and accessible equipment

- wide dissemination of information about accessible facilities

- awareness-training about disability and impairment, and the diverse needs of disabled people

- the provision of extra help on hand for disabled people, as necessary, including specialist staff

- options for both inclusive and disabled-only provision and flexibility to respond to users' needs in the range of options of activity type, and of level of assistance.

Appendices

Appendix 1: Sample profile

Interview type		Total	In-depth interviews	Focus groups
Total		62	40	22
Men		29	17	12
Women		33	23	10
Physical impairment		16	11	5
wheelchair users	9			
non-wheelchair users	7			
Visual impairment		16	12	4
Hearing impairment		15	15	
BSL users	7			
non-BSL users	8			
Learning difficulty		15	2	13
Disabled from birth/childhood*		16	12	4
Disabled later in life		31	26	5
18–29 years		15	9	6
30–39		15	8	7
40–49		16	9	7
50–59		9	8	1
60–70		7	6	1
Inactive		47	33	14
Active		15	7	8
Nottinghamshire		15	11	4
Yorkshire		12	12	
London and South-East		29	11	18
Other	6	6		
Working	14	9	5	
Training/student	7	7		
Not working/retired	41	24	17	

*not learning difficulty group

In addition, one focus group was carried out with eight parent carers of people with learning disabilities. These were all women, and their age range was estimated to span from 30 to 70.

More than one impairment type:
Four of the respondents with physical impairments also had sensory impairments.

Three of the hearing impairment group also had physical impairments – with two of these the physical condition (heart attack) appeared to predominate.

Three of the visual impairment group also had physical impairments, again with two of these respondents the physical condition appeared to predominate.

A number of the respondents also had speech impairments or other secondary disabling conditions in addition to their 'main' impairment, for example asthma, epilepsy, high blood pressure.

Respondents are grouped according to the impairment type for which they were initially selected, although experiences related to other impairments have been used where specific to that impairment.

Appendix 2: Details of research methodology

Consultation stage

Consultation was carried out with the following organisations. The extent of consultation ranged from telephone conversations to taped meetings.

Disability Sport England
SCOPE
Royal National Institute for the Blind
British Deaf Association
Royal National Institute for the Deaf
British Institute for People with Learning Difficulties (BILD)
English Sports Association (for people with learning disability)

The objectives of the consultation stage were:

- to raise awareness and an understanding of possible issues

- to identify any existing research or literature

- to explore sampling issues and options

- to discuss potential access problems, for example, communication methods, use of venues.

Sample selection and parameters

Definitions of whether someone is classified as disabled are notoriously complex, as is reflected in research studies and in assessment procedures used to decide whether someone qualifies for a particular service or social security benefit. It was agreed with the HEA that the focus of the study should be on disabled people whose impairment could be said to have a significant effect on their daily living. This was done in order to try to ensure that the selected respondents could contribute the maximum amount of data in terms of their experiences of barriers and difficulties.

Quota controls were designed at the time of recruitment to ensure diversity within the sample overall and, to a lesser extent, within each of the four impairment groups. These ensured diversity on the basis of:

- age

- sex

- nature of impairment (for physically and hearing impaired only).

No specific quotas were set for other characteristics, although checks were made to ensure that there was a range of severity of impairment, and whether respondents were working or not. Locations for recruitment were also selected with the aim of reflecting a range in terms of social background.

Fieldwork structure

It was agreed that the research design should mainly be based on in-depth interviews, supplemented by focus groups. In addition, it was decided that a focus group with deaf and hearing impaired people would not be appropriate as communication barriers would mean the open exchange of views may be impeded. For people with learning difficulties, it was decided that the best interview format would be small groups, based on previous research with this group. Previous experience has also indicated that establishing an initial relationship and then returning to carry out discussions is a good way to carry out a successful interview. We were able to use the opportunity of one of the research team having recently carried out some interviewing with people with learning difficulties to return to the same day centre.

The main part of the fieldwork was divided between three locations – the London area, Nottinghamshire and Yorkshire. In addition, six of the interviews with deaf respondents were carried out at the BDA annual conference.

Recruitment

A variety of methods were used, with the majority of respondents being recruited in the community by knocking on doors in the selected localities. This included asking people about any disabled people living in the area, and also looking for any obvious indicators such as disabled car badges. At an early stage, it was found that some people were very anxious about being asked about their receipt of disability benefits – this had been included in the recruitment interview to provide a broad indicator of severity of disability. This subject was left out in subsequent recruitment exercises.

In addition to door-knocking, the following recruitment methods were carried out for the different impairment groups:

Physically impaired:

- – one in-depth interview and one group at a disability sports association
- – two in-depth interviews at an independent living scheme

Visually impaired:

- – one group at a local Royal Society for the Blind
- – five in-depth interviews at a local training centre for blind people

Hearing impaired:

- – six respondents attending the BDA annual conference

Learning disabilities:

- – one in-depth interview at supported accommodation
- – three small groups (between 3–6 people) and one interview recruited
at a local day centre;
group of parent carers recruited at local day centre

Conduct of study

Interviews and groups were carried out in respondents' homes or in day centres or training centres. A sign language interpreter was used to carry out interviews for people who use British Sign Language (BSL). All interviews were carried out by members of SCPR's Qualitative Research Unit, chosen because they were experienced in working with disabled people. All interviews and discussions were tape recorded, with the permission of the respondents, and transcribed verbatim for analysis.

A small number of respondents were interviewed with a partner present who made a small contribution to the interview. In each case, the partner was also disabled, but as the contribution they made was minor, they have not been included in the sample profile. In one interview, both husband and wife made an equal contribution to the interview, and have, therefore, both been included in sample details.

Topic guide

A list of issues to be covered in the interviews and focus groups was developed by the researchers in conjunction with the HEA. It drew on issues that had been found to be pertinent in other research studies investigating attitudes to physical activity. This topic guide was used as a broad framework for exploring a wide range of issues. The topic guide was also adapted slightly to include appropriate areas of questioning for people with different impairment types. Although based on a common framework, the style of questioning used was responsive to the individual circumstances and experiences at the time of the interview or focus group.

Analysis

Based on both tape recordings and the verbatim transcripts, a detailed content analysis of the qualitative data was undertaken. Analytical charts were constructed from these, synthesising the beliefs, attitudes, behaviours and experiences of the respondents in relation to each of the issues, identifying recurrent themes or patterns of association within the data. A set of charts was drawn up for each focus group and for each of the in-depth interviews, structured according to key issues. Such charts, together with illustrative material taken verbatim from the interviews, form the basis of this report.

Copies of the fieldwork documents are included in Appendix 3.

Appendix 3: Fieldwork documents

Topic guide

P5829 Disabled people and physical activity October 1998

Topic guide for people with physical disabilities

To explore:

- awareness of the health benefits of physical activity
- attitudes towards participation in physical activity
- barriers to participation
- motivations
- ways of overcoming barriers.

Introduction

- Research for the Health Education Authority.
- To explore: attitudes to exercise and physical activity and barriers to doing it.
- Stress confidentiality.

1. Background

- Age
- Household
- Working status, day-time activity
- How normally get about – transport?
  - wheelchair user?
  - aid of a stick?
- How much normally get about

2. Activity levels now

- Physical activity, if any, done nowadays
  - what
  - how often (part of routine?); level of intensity
  - where/alone or with others
- Likes and dislikes of doing this
- How normally get about – car, walk, bicycle, bus

3. Perception of 'physical activity'? *[BRIEF]*

- What included when think of physical activity
  - type of activity (housework, dancing, walking, gardening, armchair aerobics, special adapted wheelchair activities, etc.)
  - reasons

4. Perceived health / fitness levels

- What do they think about their level of health and fitness?

- Anything about their health / disability that prevents them from being physically active?

- Do they think they should be any less fit because of their impairment?

5. Activity levels *in the past*

- How does their activity level now compare to activity in the past?
  - And cf. childhood/school/other past activities?
    If severe disability: Integrated in mainstream school, or special school for people with disabilities?
    Integrated or segregated and feelings about this
    What done then (including therapeutic activities)
    How got involved – relative roles of different people / organisations
    How felt about this past physical activity?
    (Did it put off or encourage?)

6. Beliefs/knowledge about physical activity

- How important is it to do physical activity? (Why?)

fitness

health (how is health different from fitness?)

confidence / sense of achievement

mental health, general well-being

reducing risk of injury

weight control

other reasons?

- Is it more or less important for them to do physical activity? (As a disabled person) Why?

- How important is physical activity *compared to other actions* that people might take to maintain their health? (Why?)

not smoking

good diet

not drinking / drugs

stress / not worrying

sleep

- *Knowledge:* In relation to physical activity, what do you need to do (re. physical activity) to be fit / healthy?

  - How often?
    What type of activity? (affecting suppleness, strength, stamina)
    How long for?
    What level of intensity? (breathlessness, feel heartbeat)

[For general health gain, HEA recommend: building up to at least Moderate level activity of any sport or activities such as brisk walking, swimming, dancing, cycling, or heavy housework, which are done:

(a) for about half an hour at a time or longer

(b) to the extent that it makes you feel warm and slightly out of breath

(c) about five times a week] PROBE REACTION TO THIS RECOMMENDATION

***Throughout this discussion:*

- How important are all these things in general [general belief] and how important to them personally [personal salience]? Alternative priorities?

- *Sources of these beliefs:*

  - Who or what influences what they think about physical activity and exercise?

family, friends, carers

day centre

media

role models

medical and other professionals

  - Effect of own experiences

7. Perceived barriers to physical activity

- Do they think they do enough physical activity? Why/why not?

- What puts them off doing more physical exercise?

- Probe all perceived barriers

- Applicable to all activities? E.g. team / individual activities

- **Are there any particular barriers to you ? Are there any things you need help with? Does this affect whether you can do physical activities at all? Or how feel about doing them?**

Past experiences
Lack of time
Lack of money
  – compared to other things

  – how much is needed, e.g. for specialist equipment

Physical access barriers
  – to buildings

  – equipment

  – transport

Need for assistance/support (formal/informal)
  – getting to venue

  – doing exercise

The type of activity offered, organisation of activity (e.g. segregated or integrated)
Communication barriers
Information barriers
  – lack of knowledge about what's available, what they could do

  – why? Gatekeepers?

Other people's attitudes
  – peers, officials, family, carers, professionals

  – formal and informal attitudinal barriers; exclusion policies

  – effects?

The nature of the disability
Confidence, self-perception, embarrassment
Fears/ concerns / worries about doing physical activity?
  – safety: doing activity and getting to activity

Lack of motivation
  – lack of energy

  – no-one to do exercise with

  – no interest

Other   **PROBE ALL FULLY**

- What would they like to do? Why? Why not done?

8. Overcoming the barriers

If / when active:

At what point – if at all – did they decide to become active despite the external / environmental barriers? (e.g. why / what makes an individual with a physical disability get someone else to carry them and their wheelchair up some steps and when / why do they simply go home?)

All:

- What would encourage them to do more physical activity? or a different type?

- How have they been encouraged in the past? By who? What sort of activity and why?

- How could barriers be overcome?
    - any preference for activity with others who have difficulties like you?
    - provision of accessible facilities, equipment, assistance, 'adapted' activities
    - more information / knowledge about options
    - other?

- What would they like about doing (more) physical activity?
  Probe for particular reasons, objectives – any particular type of activity

- How do active people overcome barriers? What motivates them to continue? What makes active people different from themselves?

- Would promotional strategies help?

9. Promotional activities

- Awareness of any information or promotional material on physical activity?
    - heard or seen anything at all (from any source)
    - what did they think about it

- Is there a need for more information or advice?
    - what kind?
    - where? how circulated?
- Who would they look to for information or advice about physical activity?

- How would they promote physical activity to deaf people (if they were the HEA)?

- What would work for them personally?

Sample Approach letter

P5829 / D

October 1998

A research study for the Health Education Authority on exercise and physical activity

Thank you for agreeing to take part in this research which is about how people regard exercise and physical activity. The study is being carried out by Social & Community Planning Research, an independent research institute. Its aim is to explore attitudes towards doing exercise, of any kind, whether housework, or playing a sport, or any physical activity. Whether or not you do physical activity, we are interested in your views.

The study is one of a series which at present is focusing on the views of people with a disability or long-term illness.

As agreed, the interviewer will call on: ....

at: .... a.m. / p.m.

The interview will last about an hour. Everything that you say will be treated as confidential: you will not be identified by name in any report on the research. We will be giving each participant £15 as a small token of thanks for your help. If you have any queries please contact me or my colleague Helen Finch on 0171 250 1866.

Yours sincerely

Sue Arthur

Project Researcher